Dairy DIARY 2019

W0009917

Name
....

Address
....

....

Postcode
....

☎ Home
....

☎ Mobile
....

Email
....

....

In case of emergency contact:
....

Name
....

☎ Tel.
....

Website: dairydiary.co.uk
Blog: dairydiary.co.uk/blog
To order: 0845 0948 128

PLANNER 2019

JANUARY		FEBRUARY	MARCH
1 Tue	BANK HOLIDAY	1 Fri	1 Fri
2 Wed	BANK HOLIDAY SCOTLAND	**2 Sat**	**2 Sat**
3 Thu		**3 Sun**	**3 Sun**
4 Fri		4 Mon	4 Mon
5 Sat		5 Tue	5 Tue
6 Sun		6 Wed	6 Wed
7 Mon		7 Thu	7 Thu
8 Tue		8 Fri	8 Fri
9 Wed		**9 Sat**	**9 Sat**
10 Thu		**10 Sun**	**10 Sun**
11 Fri		11 Mon	11 Mon
12 Sat		12 Tue	12 Tue
13 Sun		13 Wed	13 Wed
14 Mon		14 Thu	14 Thu
15 Tue		15 Fri	15 Fri
16 Wed		**16 Sat**	**16 Sat**
17 Thu		**17 Sun**	**17 Sun**
18 Fri		18 Mon	18 Mon BANK HOLIDAY N. IRELAND
19 Sat		19 Tue	19 Tue
20 Sun		20 Wed	20 Wed
21 Mon		21 Thu	21 Thu
22 Tue		22 Fri	22 Fri
23 Wed		**23 Sat**	**23 Sat**
24 Thu		**24 Sun**	**24 Sun**
25 Fri		25 Mon	25 Mon
26 Sat		26 Tue	26 Tue
27 Sun		27 Wed	27 Wed
28 Mon		28 Thu	28 Thu
29 Tue			29 Fri
30 Wed			**30 Sat**
31 Thu			**31 Sun**

APRIL		MAY		JUNE	
1	Mon	1	Wed	**1**	**Sat**
2	Tue	2	Thu	**2**	**Sun**
3	Wed	3	Fri	3	Mon
4	Thu	**4**	**Sat**	4	Tue
5	Fri	**5**	**Sun**	5	Wed
6	**Sat**	6	Mon BANK HOLIDAY	6	Thu
7	**Sun**	7	Tue	7	Fri
8	Mon	8	Wed	**8**	**Sat**
9	Tue	9	Thu	**9**	**Sun**
10	Wed	10	Fri	10	Mon
11	Thu	**11**	**Sat**	11	Tue
12	Fri	**12**	**Sun**	12	Wed
13	**Sat**	13	Mon	13	Thu
14	**Sun**	14	Tue	14	Fri
15	Mon	15	Wed	**15**	**Sat**
16	Tue	16	Thu	**16**	**Sun**
17	Wed	17	Fri	17	Mon
18	Thu	**18**	**Sat**	18	Tue
19	Fri BANK HOLIDAY	**19**	**Sun**	19	Wed
20	**Sat**	20	Mon	20	Thu
21	**Sun**	21	Tue	21	Fri
22	Mon BANK HOLIDAY	22	Wed	**22**	**Sat**
23	Tue	23	Thu	**23**	**Sun**
24	Wed	24	Fri	24	Mon
25	Thu	**25**	**Sat**	25	Tue
26	Fri	**26**	**Sun**	26	Wed
27	**Sat**	27	Mon BANK HOLIDAY	27	Thu
28	**Sun**	28	Tue	28	Fri
29	Mon	29	Wed	**29**	**Sat**
30	Tue	30	Thu	**30**	**Sun**
		31	Fri		

PLANNER 2019

JULY	AUGUST	SEPTEMBER
1 Mon	1 Thu	**1 Sun**
2 Tue	2 Fri	2 Mon
3 Wed	**3 Sat**	3 Tue
4 Thu	**4 Sun**	4 Wed
5 Fri	5 Mon BANK HOLIDAY SCOTLAND	5 Thu
6 Sat	6 Tue	6 Fri
7 Sun	7 Wed	**7 Sat**
8 Mon	8 Thu	**8 Sun**
9 Tue	9 Fri	9 Mon
10 Wed	**10 Sat**	10 Tue
11 Thu	**11 Sun**	11 Wed
12 Fri BANK HOLIDAY N. IRELAND	12 Mon	12 Thu
13 Sat	13 Tue	13 Fri
14 Sun	14 Wed	**14 Sat**
15 Mon	15 Thu	**15 Sun**
16 Tue	16 Fri	16 Mon
17 Wed	**17 Sat**	17 Tue
18 Thu	**18 Sun**	18 Wed
19 Fri	19 Mon	19 Thu
20 Sat	20 Tue	20 Fri
21 Sun	21 Wed	**21 Sat**
22 Mon	22 Thu	**22 Sun**
23 Tue	23 Fri	23 Mon
24 Wed	**24 Sat**	24 Tue
25 Thu	**25 Sun**	25 Wed
26 Fri	26 Mon BANK HOLIDAY	26 Thu
27 Sat	27 Tue	27 Fri
28 Sun	28 Wed	**28 Sat**
29 Mon	29 Thu	**29 Sun**
30 Tue	30 Fri	30 Mon
31 Wed	**31 Sat**	

OCTOBER		NOVEMBER		DECEMBER	
1	Tue	1	Fri	**1**	**Sun**
2	Wed	**2**	**Sat**	2	Mon
3	Thu	**3**	**Sun**	3	Tue
4	Fri	4	Mon	4	Wed
5	**Sat**	5	Tue	5	Thu
6	**Sun**	6	Wed	6	Fri
7	Mon	7	Thu	**7**	**Sat**
8	Tue	8	Fri	**8**	**Sun**
9	Wed	**9**	**Sat**	9	Mon
10	Thu	**10**	**Sun**	10	Tue
11	Fri	11	Mon	11	Wed
12	**Sat**	12	Tue	12	Thu
13	**Sun**	13	Wed	13	Fri
14	Mon	14	Thu	**14**	**Sat**
15	Tue	15	Fri	**15**	**Sun**
16	Wed	**16**	**Sat**	16	Mon
17	Thu	**17**	**Sun**	17	Tue
18	Fri	18	Mon	18	Wed
19	**Sat**	19	Tue	19	Thu
20	**Sun**	20	Wed	20	Fri
21	Mon	21	Thu	**21**	**Sat**
22	Tue	22	Fri	**22**	**Sun**
23	Wed	**23**	**Sat**	23	Mon
24	Thu	**24**	**Sun**	24	Tue
25	Fri	25	Mon	25	Wed — BANK HOLIDAY
26	**Sat**	26	Tue	26	Thu — BANK HOLIDAY
27	**Sun**	27	Wed	27	Fri
28	Mon	28	Thu	**28**	**Sat**
29	Tue	29	Fri	**29**	**Sun**
30	Wed	**30**	**Sat**	30	Mon
31	Thu			31	Tue

Contents

Exercise for fun 26

Live more with less 28

Recipes & tips online 30

Garden tricks 32

Flower & foodie fairs 36

Cheese glorious cheese 40

Choose cheese 44

USEFUL REMINDERS

PERSONAL

Bank

Beauty therapist

Building Society

Citizen's Advice   citizensadvice.org.uk

  for England   03444 111 444

  for Wales   03444 77 20 20

Credit card emergency 1

Credit card emergency 2

Hairdresser

Life insurance policy number

  ☎ contact

  renewal date

Samaritans   116 123 (or local branch)

      samaritans.org

Solicitor

Work

Other

Other

Other

Other

HEALTH

Blood group

Chemist

Chiropodist

Dentist

Doctor

Hospital

Medical insurance policy number

  ☎ contact

  renewal date

National insurance number

NHS (non-emergency)   111 nhs.uk

NHS number

Optician

Other

Other

Other

Other

Other

Other

Notes

8

HOME

Boiler service date

Childminder/nursery

Council

Electrician

Electricity provider

Gas engineer

Gas provider

Home insurance policy number

☎ contact

renewal date

Plumber

Police (non-emergency)   101   police.uk

School

TV licence renewal date

Vet

Water provider

Other

Other

Other

Other

Other

Other

Other

Other

TRAVEL

Car insurance policy number

☎ contact

renewal date

Breakdown service

Driving licence number

Garage

MOT due date

Road tax renewal date

Service date

Vehicle registration number

Eurostar   03432 186 186   eurostar.com

National Rail enq   0345 748 4950

nationalrail.co.uk

Taxi

Passport adviceline   0300 222 0000

gov.uk/passport-advice-line

Passport number

renewal date

EHIC number

renewal date

Travel agent

Travel insurance policy number

☎ contact

renewal date

Other

9

FAMILY & FRIENDS

Name

Address

☎ Home

  Work

  Mobile

Email

Name

Address

☎ Home

  Work

  Mobile

Email

Name

Address

☎ Home

  Work

  Mobile

Email

Name

Address

☎ Home

  Work

  Mobile

Email

Name

Address

☎ Home

  Work

  Mobile

Email

Name

Address

☎ Home

  Work

  Mobile

Email

Name

Address

☎ Home

Work

Mobile

Email

Name

Address

☎ Home

Work

Mobile

Email

Name

Address

☎ Home

Work

Mobile

Email

Name

Address

☎ Home

Work

Mobile

Email

Name

Address

☎ Home

Work

Mobile

Email

Name

Address

☎ Home

Work

Mobile

Email

FAMILY & FRIENDS

Name

Address

☎ Home

  Work

  Mobile

Email

Name

Address

☎ Home

  Work

  Mobile

Email

Name

Address

☎ Home

  Work

  Mobile

Email

Name

Address

☎ Home

  Work

  Mobile

Email

Name

Address

☎ Home

  Work

  Mobile

Email

Name

Address

☎ Home

  Work

  Mobile

Email

FAMILY & FRIENDS

Name

Address

☎ Home

Work

Mobile

Email

Name

Address

☎ Home

Work

Mobile

Email

Name

Address

☎ Home

Work

Mobile

Email

Name

Address

☎ Home

Work

Mobile

Email

Name

Address

☎ Home

Work

Mobile

Email

Name

Address

☎ Home

Work

Mobile

Email

HOME BUDGETING

	JANUARY	FEBRUARY	MARCH
Opening balance			
Income			
New balance			
Birthdays/Christmas			
Car insurance			
Car MOT/service/tax			
Childcare			
Clothing/shoes			
Council tax			
Dentist/optician			
Electricity			
Entertainment			
Gas/oil/solid fuel			
Groceries			
Hairdresser			
Holidays			
Home/pet insurance			
Life/medical insurance			
Mobile/phone/internet			
Mortgage/rent			
Newspapers/magazines			
Petrol/fares			
Pets			
Savings			
TV licence/satellite			
Water			
Other			
Other			
Other			
Total expenditure			
Closing balance			

	APRIL	MAY	JUNE
Opening balance			
Income			
New balance			
Birthdays/Christmas			
Car insurance			
Car MOT/service/tax			
Childcare			
Clothing/shoes			
Council tax			
Dentist/optician			
Electricity			
Entertainment			
Gas/oil/solid fuel			
Groceries			
Hairdresser			
Holidays			
Home/pet insurance			
Life/medical insurance			
Mobile/phone/internet			
Mortgage/rent			
Newspapers/magazines			
Petrol/fares			
Pets			
Savings			
TV licence/satellite			
Water			
Other			
Other			
Other			
Total expenditure			
Closing balance			

HOME BUDGETING

	JULY	AUGUST	SEPTEMBER
Opening balance			
Income			
New balance			
Birthdays/Christmas			
Car insurance			
Car MOT/service/tax			
Childcare			
Clothing/shoes			
Council tax			
Dentist/optician			
Electricity			
Entertainment			
Gas/oil/solid fuel			
Groceries			
Hairdresser			
Holidays			
Home/pet insurance			
Life/medical insurance			
Mobile/phone/internet			
Mortgage/rent			
Newspapers/magazines			
Petrol/fares			
Pets			
Savings			
TV licence/satellite			
Water			
Other			
Other			
Other			
Total expenditure			
Closing balance			

	OCTOBER	NOVEMBER	DECEMBER
Opening balance			
Income			
New balance			
Birthdays/Christmas			
Car insurance			
Car MOT/service/tax			
Childcare			
Clothing/shoes			
Council tax			
Dentist/optician			
Electricity			
Entertainment			
Gas/oil/solid fuel			
Groceries			
Hairdresser			
Holidays			
Home/pet insurance			
Life/medical insurance			
Mobile/phone/internet			
Mortgage/rent			
Newspapers/magazines			
Petrol/fares			
Pets			
Savings			
TV licence/satellite			
Water			
Other			
Other			
Other			
Total expenditure			
Closing balance			

2018

January

Mon	1	8	15	22	29
Tue	2	9	16	23	30
Wed	3	10	17	24	31
Thu	4	11	18	25	
Fri	5	12	19	26	
Sat	6	13	20	27	
Sun	7	14	21	28	

February

Mon		5	12	19	26
Tue		6	13	20	27
Wed		7	14	21	28
Thu	1	8	15	22	
Fri	2	9	16	23	
Sat	3	10	17	24	
Sun	4	11	18	25	

March

Mon		5	12	19	26
Tue		6	13	20	27
Wed		7	14	21	28
Thu	1	8	15	22	29
Fri	2	9	16	23	30
Sat	3	10	17	24	31
Sun	4	11	18	25	

April

Mon	2	9	16	23	30
Tue	3	10	17	24	
Wed	4	11	18	25	
Thu	5	12	19	26	
Fri	6	13	20	27	
Sat	7	14	21	28	
Sun	1	8	15	22	29

May

Mon		7	14	21	28
Tue	1	8	15	22	29
Wed	2	9	16	23	30
Thu	3	10	17	24	31
Fri	4	11	18	25	
Sat	5	12	19	26	
Sun	6	13	20	27	

June

Mon		4	11	18	25
Tue		5	12	19	26
Wed		6	13	20	27
Thu		7	14	21	28
Fri	1	8	15	22	29
Sat	2	9	16	23	30
Sun	3	10	17	24	

July

Mon	2	9	16	23	30
Tue	3	10	17	24	31
Wed	4	11	18	25	
Thu	5	12	19	26	
Fri	6	13	20	27	
Sat	7	14	21	28	
Sun	1	8	15	22	29

August

Mon		6	13	20	27
Tue		7	14	21	28
Wed	1	8	15	22	29
Thu	2	9	16	23	30
Fri	3	10	17	24	31
Sat	4	11	18	25	
Sun	5	12	19	26	

September

Mon		3	10	17	24
Tue		4	11	18	25
Wed		5	12	19	26
Thu		6	13	20	27
Fri		7	14	21	28
Sat	1	8	15	22	29
Sun	2	9	16	23	30

October

Mon	1	8	15	22	29
Tue	2	9	16	23	30
Wed	3	10	17	24	31
Thu	4	11	18	25	
Fri	5	12	19	26	
Sat	6	13	20	27	
Sun	7	14	21	28	

November

Mon		5	12	19	26
Tue		6	13	20	27
Wed		7	14	21	28
Thu	1	8	15	22	29
Fri	2	9	16	23	30
Sat	3	10	17	24	
Sun	4	11	18	25	

December

Mon		3	10	17	24	31
Tue		4	11	18	25	
Wed		5	12	19	26	
Thu		6	13	20	27	
Fri		7	14	21	28	
Sat	1	8	15	22	29	
Sun	2	9	16	23	30	

2020

January

Mon		6	13	20	27
Tue		7	14	21	28
Wed	1	8	15	22	29
Thu	2	9	16	23	30
Fri	3	10	17	24	31
Sat	4	11	18	25	
Sun	5	12	19	26	

February

Mon		3	10	17	24
Tue		4	11	18	25
Wed		5	12	19	26
Thu		6	13	20	27
Fri		7	14	21	28
Sat	1	8	15	22	29
Sun	2	9	16	23	

March

Mon		2	9	16	23	30
Tue		3	10	17	24	31
Wed		4	11	18	25	
Thu		5	12	19	26	
Fri		6	13	20	27	
Sat		7	14	21	28	
Sun	1	8	15	22	29	

April

Mon		6	13	20	27
Tue		7	14	21	28
Wed	1	8	15	22	29
Thu	2	9	16	23	30
Fri	3	10	17	24	
Sat	4	11	18	25	
Sun	5	12	19	26	

May

Mon		4	11	18	25
Tue		5	12	19	26
Wed		6	13	20	27
Thu		7	14	21	28
Fri	1	8	15	22	29
Sat	2	9	16	23	30
Sun	3	10	17	24	31

June

Mon	1	8	15	22	29
Tue	2	9	16	23	30
Wed	3	10	17	24	
Thu	4	11	18	25	
Fri	5	12	19	26	
Sat	6	13	20	27	
Sun	7	14	21	28	

July

Mon		6	13	20	27
Tue		7	14	21	28
Wed	1	8	15	22	29
Thu	2	9	16	23	30
Fri	3	10	17	24	31
Sat	4	11	18	25	
Sun	5	12	19	26	

August

Mon		3	10	17	24	31
Tue		4	11	18	25	
Wed		5	12	19	26	
Thu		6	13	20	27	
Fri		7	14	21	28	
Sat	1	8	15	22	29	
Sun	2	9	16	23	30	

September

Mon		7	14	21	28
Tue	1	8	15	22	29
Wed	2	9	16	23	30
Thu	3	10	17	24	
Fri	4	11	18	25	
Sat	5	12	19	26	
Sun	6	13	20	27	

October

Mon		5	12	19	26
Tue		6	13	20	27
Wed		7	14	21	28
Thu	1	8	15	22	29
Fri	2	9	16	23	30
Sat	3	10	17	24	31
Sun	4	11	18	25	

November

Mon		2	9	16	23	30
Tue		3	10	17	24	
Wed		4	11	18	25	
Thu		5	12	19	26	
Fri		6	13	20	27	
Sat		7	14	21	28	
Sun	1	8	15	22	29	

December

Mon		7	14	21	28
Tue	1	8	15	22	29
Wed	2	9	16	23	30
Thu	3	10	17	24	31
Fri	4	11	18	25	
Sat	5	12	19	26	
Sun	6	13	20	27	

2019

January

Mon		7	14	21	28
Tue	1	8	15	22	29
Wed	2	9	16	23	30
Thu	3	10	17	24	31
Fri	4	11	18	25	
Sat	5	12	19	26	
Sun	6	13	20	27	

February

Mon		4	11	18	25
Tue		5	12	19	26
Wed		6	13	20	27
Thu		7	14	21	28
Fri	1	8	15	22	
Sat	2	9	16	23	
Sun	3	10	17	24	

March

Mon		4	11	18	25
Tue		5	12	19	26
Wed		6	13	20	27
Thu		7	14	21	28
Fri	1	8	15	22	29
Sat	2	9	16	23	30
Sun	3	10	17	24	31

April

Mon	1	8	15	22	29
Tue	2	9	16	23	30
Wed	3	10	17	24	
Thu	4	11	18	25	
Fri	5	12	19	26	
Sat	6	13	20	27	
Sun	7	14	21	28	

May

Mon		6	13	20	27
Tue		7	14	21	28
Wed	1	8	15	22	29
Thu	2	9	16	23	30
Fri	3	10	17	24	31
Sat	4	11	18	25	
Sun	5	12	19	26	

June

Mon		3	10	17	24
Tue		4	11	18	25
Wed		5	12	19	26
Thu		6	13	20	27
Fri		7	14	21	28
Sat	1	8	15	22	29
Sun	2	9	16	23	30

July

Mon	1	8	15	22	29
Tue	2	9	16	23	30
Wed	3	10	17	24	31
Thu	4	11	18	25	
Fri	5	12	19	26	
Sat	6	13	20	27	
Sun	7	14	21	28	

August

Mon		5	12	19	26
Tue		6	13	20	27
Wed		7	14	21	28
Thu	1	8	15	22	29
Fri	2	9	16	23	30
Sat	3	10	17	24	31
Sun	4	11	18	25	

September

Mon		2	9	16	23	30
Tue		3	10	17	24	
Wed		4	11	18	25	
Thu		5	12	19	26	
Fri		6	13	20	27	
Sat		7	14	21	28	
Sun	1	8	15	22	29	

October

Mon		7	14	21	28
Tue	1	8	15	22	29
Wed	2	9	16	23	30
Thu	3	10	17	24	31
Fri	4	11	18	25	
Sat	5	12	19	26	
Sun	6	13	20	27	

November

Mon		4	11	18	25
Tue		5	12	19	26
Wed		6	13	20	27
Thu		7	14	21	28
Fri	1	8	15	22	29
Sat	2	9	16	23	30
Sun	3	10	17	24	

December

Mon		2	9	16	23	30
Tue		3	10	17	24	31
Wed		4	11	18	25	
Thu		5	12	19	26	
Fri		6	13	20	27	
Sat		7	14	21	28	
Sun	1	8	15	22	29	

Calendar dates

UK HOLIDAYS †	2019	2020
New Year	Jan 1	Jan 1
New Year (Scotland)	Jan 1/2	Jan 1/2
St Patrick's Day (Northern Ireland)	Mar 18*	Mar 17
Good Friday	Apr 19	Apr 10
Easter Monday (except Scotland)	Apr 22	Apr 13
Early Spring	May 6	May 4
Spring	May 27	May 25
Battle of the Boyne (Northern Ireland)	Jul 12	Jul 13*
Summer (Scotland)	Aug 5	Aug 3
Summer (except Scotland)	Aug 26	Aug 31
Christmas Day	Dec 25	Dec 25
Boxing Day	Dec 26	Dec 28*

NOTABLE DATES	2019
Burns' Night	Jan 25
Holocaust Memorial Day	Jan 27
Chinese New Year – Year of the Pig	Feb 5
Accession of Queen Elizabeth II	Feb 6
St Valentine's Day	Feb 14
St David's Day (Wales)	Mar 1
Shrove Tuesday (Pancake Day)	Mar 5
Commonwealth Day	Mar 11
St Patrick's Day (Ireland)	Mar 17
Mothering Sunday	Mar 31
Birthday of Queen Elizabeth II	Apr 21
St George's Day (England)	Apr 23
World Red Cross/Red Crescent Day	May 8
Coronation Day	Jun 2
Queen's Official Birthday (t.b.c.)	Jun 8
Father's Day	Jun 16
Armed Forces' Day	Jun 29
St Swithin's Day	Jul 15
International Day of Peace	Sep 21
United Nations Day	Oct 24
Halloween	Oct 31
Remembrance Sunday	Nov 10
Armistice Day	Nov 11
Birthday of the Prince of Wales	Nov 14
St Andrew's Day (Scotland)	Nov 30

RELIGIOUS DATES

Christian

Epiphany	Jan 6
Ash Wednesday	Mar 6
Palm Sunday	Apr 14
Good Friday	Apr 19
Easter Day	Apr 21
Ascension Day	May 30
Whit Sunday, Pentecost	Jun 9
Trinity Sunday	Jun 16
Corpus Christi	Jun 20
Advent Sunday	Dec 1
Christmas Day	Dec 25

Buddhist

Parinirvana Day	Feb 8
Wesak (Buddha Day)	May 18
Bodhi Day (Buddha's enlightenment)	Dec 8

Hindu

Maha Shivaratri	Mar 4
Holi	Mar 21
Navaratri begins	Sep 29
Diwali begins (also celebrated by Sikhs)	Oct 27

Islamic

Ramadan begins	May 6
Eid Ul-Fitr	Jun 5
Eid Ul-Adha	Aug 12
Al-Hijra (New Year)	Sep 1
Milad un Nabi (Prophet's birthday)	Nov 10

Jewish

Purim begins	Mar 21
Pesach (Passover) begins	Apr 20
Shavuot (Pentecost) begins	Jun 9
Rosh Hashanah (Jewish New Year)	Sep 30
Yom Kippur (Day of Atonement)	Oct 9
Succoth (Tabernacles) begins	Oct 14
Chanukah begins	Dec 23

Sikh

These dates follow the Nanakshahi calendar

Birthday of Guru Gobind Singh	Jan 5
Vaisakhi	Apr 14
Birthday of Guru Nanak	Apr 15
Martyrdom of Guru Arjan Dev	Jun 16
Martyrdom of Guru Tegh Bahadur	Nov 24

Note: Many religious dates are based on the lunar calendar and, therefore, we cannot guarantee their accuracy.

†Bank Holiday dates can change
*Substitute Bank Holidays – St Patrick's Day falls on a Sunday in 2019, and Boxing Day falls on a Saturday in 2020.

PHASES OF THE MOON

● New moon

	Day	H:M
Jan	6	01:28
Feb	4	21:04
Mar	6	16:04
Apr	5	08:50
May	4	22:46
Jun	3	10:02
Jul	2	19:16
Aug	1	03:12
Aug	30	10:37
Sep	28	18:26
Oct	28	03:38
Nov	26	15:06
Dec	26	05:13

) First quarter

	Day	H:M
Jan	14	06:46
Feb	12	22:26
Mar	14	10:27
Apr	12	19:06
May	12	01:12
Jun	10	05:59
Jul	9	10:55
Aug	7	17:31
Sep	6	03:10
Oct	5	16:47
Nov	4	10:23
Dec	4	06:58

○ Full moon

	Day	H:M
Jan	21	05:16
Feb	19	15:54
Mar	21	01:43
Apr	19	11:12
May	18	21:11
Jun	17	08:31
Jul	16	21:38
Aug	15	12:29
Sep	14	04:33
Oct	13	21:08
Nov	12	13:34
Dec	12	05:12

(Last quarter

	Day	H:M
Jan	27	21:10
Feb	26	11:28
Mar	28	04:10
Apr	26	22:18
May	26	16:34
Jun	25	09:46
Jul	25	01:18
Aug	23	14:56
Sep	22	02:41
Oct	21	12:39
Nov	19	21:11
Dec	19	04:57

BRITISH SUMMERTIME

▶ Clocks go forward 1 hour at 1am on 31 March

◀ Clocks go back 1 hour at 2am on 27 October

SEASONS

	Month	Day	H:M
Vernal equinox Spring begins	Mar	20	21:58
Summer solstice Summer begins	June	21	15:54
Autumnal equinox Autumn begins	Sep	23	07:50
Winter solstice Winter begins	Dec	22	04:19

WEBSITES

gov.uk/bank-holidays

when-is.com

SUNRISE AND SUNSET TIMES

Note: times vary – these are for London

Day	Rise H:M	Set H:M	Day	Rise H:M	Set H:M	Day	Rise H:M	Set H:M	Day	Rise H:M	Set H:M
January			**February**			**March**			**April**		
07	08:05	16:09	07	07:30	17:00	07	06:33	17:51	07	06:23	19:43
14	08:00	16:19	14	07:17	17:13	14	06:18	18:03	14	06:08	19:55
21	07:54	16:30	21	07:03	17:26	21	06:02	18:15	21	05:53	20:07
28	07:45	16:42	28	06:49	17:38	28	05:46	18:27	28	05:39	20:18
May			**June**			**July**			**August**		
07	05:22	20:33	07	04:45	21:14	07	04:52	21:18	07	05:33	20:39
14	05:11	20:44	14	04:43	21:19	14	04:59	21:13	14	05:44	20:26
21	05:01	20:54	21	04:43	21:21	21	05:08	21:05	21	05:55	20:11
28	04:53	21:03	28	04:46	21:22	28	05:18	20:55	28	06:06	19:56
September			**October**			**November**			**December**		
07	06:22	19:34	07	07:10	18:26	07	07:04	16:24	07	07:51	15:52
14	06:33	19:18	14	07:22	18:10	14	07:16	16:13	14	07:58	15:51
21	06:44	19:02	21	07:34	17:55	21	07:28	16:04	21	08:04	15:53
28	06:56	18:46	28	06:46	16:42	28	07:39	15:57	28	08:06	15:58

NATIONAL LOTTERY
25 years/450 years

'It could be you!' A large pointing finger encouraged folk to rush for tickets and on 19 November 1994, 22 million watched Noel Edmonds host the first National Lottery draw, live on TV. A £1 ticket gave a one-in-14-million chance of correctly guessing the winning six out of 49 numbers, and seven winners shared the jackpot, receiving £839,254 each. Since then the National Lottery has expanded to include Euromillions, scratch cards and several other ways to gamble on making a fortune, but the division of funds has remained the same – half goes in prizes, 28% goes to 'good causes', 12% in government duty, 5% in commission to retailers and 5% to the operator.

It's all a far cry from the first recorded lottery draw in England, which took place on 11 January 1569 outside St Paul's Cathedral – Elizabeth I needed money for shipbuilding. Tickets went on sale in 1567 costing 10 shillings (50p) each, a tidy sum in those days.

The top prize was an amazing £5,000, to be paid partly in 'ready money' and the rest in tapestries, silver and 'good linen cloth', and all ticket holders got a prize of some sort. It wouldn't happen today!

2019 MILESTONES

350: Samuel Pepys makes his last diary entry, citing poor eyesight (31 May 1669)

300: Publication of Robinson Crusoe (25 April 1719)

200: Birth of Henry Tate, of Tate & Lyle, founder of the Tate Gallery (11 March 1819)

175: The Glaciarium, the world's first mechanically frozen ice rink, opens in London (June 1844)

150: Birth of conductor Henry Wood (3 March 1869)

150: Founding of Girton College, Cambridge, England's first residential college for women (16 October 1869)

125: The Manchester Ship Canal officially opened by Queen Victoria (21 May 1894)

125: Britain's first cable car operates across Devil's Dyke in the South Downs (1894)

125: Death of Robert Louis Stevenson (3 December 1894)

100: The Treaty of Versailles formally ends the First World War (28 June 1919)

100: George V proclaims Armistice (later Remembrance) Day; first two minutes' silence (7 November 1919)

100: Lady Astor is elected an MP and becomes the first woman to sit in the House of Commons (1 December 1919)

75: PAYE (Pay as you earn) introduced (10 February 1944)

75: Lifting of prohibition on married women working as teachers (10 March 1944)

75: D-Day Normandy landings (6 June 1944)

75: First V2 rocket attack, on London (8 September 1944)

50: The Beatles' last public performance, an impromptu concert on the roof of Apple Records in London, broken up by police (30 January 1969)

50: Kray twins found guilty of murder (4 March 1969)

50: Sir Robin Knox-Johnston completes the first solo non-stop circumnavigation of the world (22 April 1969)

50: Concorde breaks the sound barrier for the first time (1 October 1969)

50: BBC unleashes 'Monty Python's Flying Circus' (5 October 1969)

50: 50p coin introduced to replace the ten-shilling note (14 October 1969)

25: The Queen and President Mitterrand open the Channel Tunnel (6 May 1994)

25: Death of dramatist Dennis Potter (7 June 1994)

25: BBC1 broadcasts the first episode of 'The Vicar of Dibley' (10 November 1994)

WEBSITES
bl.uk
theblackpooltower.com
historynet.com
national-lottery.co.uk

BLACKPOOL TOWER

125 years: Blackpool Tower buildings, Grade I listed, opened on 14 May 1894, including ballroom, circus and aquarium (now the dungeon) as well as the 518ft (158m) tall steel and cast-iron Tower, cunningly constructed so that, should it ever topple, it would fall into the sea. Three thousand visitors converged on the new attraction, paying sixpence (2½p) entrance and another sixpence to take the lift to the top, where now a glass skywalk adds to the experience. Back on the ground, the Circus was extra. It has not missed a season since then, although the interior was redone in 1900 by eminent theatre designer Frank Matcham.

When the richly distinctive tones of the mighty Wurlitzer organ strike up, you couldn't be anywhere else but in the fabulously ornate Tower Ballroom. The dancing public still flock here to glide around the famous sprung dance floor, where 'Strictly' competitors have leaped and twirled, and bygone dancers have tripped the light fantastic since 1899. Non-dancers can sit in one of the balconies, amid all that Frank Matcham designed gorgeousness, and take afternoon tea. From time to time, the dazzling chandeliers are lowered for cleaning, which takes a week for each one.

The painting of the Tower, which goes on continuously, takes seven years, and it all started when John Bickerstaffe, Mayor of Blackpool, went to the Great Exhibition in Paris in 1889, saw the newly constructed Eiffel Tower, and wanted one.

ALCOCK AND BROWN

100 years: On14/15 June 1919, John Alcock, pilot, and Arthur Whitten Brown, navigator, made history by being the first to fly non-stop across the Atlantic, taking off from Lester's Field, St Johns, Newfoundland, and landing in a bog in Clifden, Connemara – from the air it had looked like a smooth green field. The flight, in an open-cockpit Vickers Vimy twin-engined biplane, modified from a First World War machine, had taken 16 hours at an average speed of 115 mph (185 km/h) and was anything

but smooth. Impossible to navigate through thick fog and cloud with a sextant – at one point they couldn't even see the propellers – it was a mixture of luck and skill that kept them on course, fortified with whiskey-laced coffee and sandwiches.

Raging storms with hail and snow added to their problems. Twice the plane nose-dived, coming perilously close to the waves before Alcock regained control. The whole endeavour had been triggered by the *Daily Mail* putting up a prize of £10,000, which manufacturer, pilot and navigator shared with the ground crew in St Johns, who had worked tirelessly to reassemble and prepare the plane. Alcock, from Manchester, and Brown, born in Glasgow to American parents, were knighted by the king.

ANNIVERSARY & BIRTHDAY GIFT RECORD

WEDDINGS

1	Paper	14	Ivory
2	Cotton	15	Crystal
3	Leather	20	China
4	Books	25	Silver
5	Wood	30	Pearl
6	Iron	35	Coral
7	Wool	40	Ruby
8	Bronze	45	Sapphire
9	Copper	50	Gold
10	Tin	55	Emerald
11	Steel	60	Diamond
12	Silk	65	Blue
	or linen		Sapphire
13	Lace	70	Platinum

BIRTHSTONES AND FLOWERS

Month	Birthstone	Flower
January	Garnet	Carnation
February	Amethyst	Violet
March	Aquamarine	Jonquil
April	Diamond	Sweet Pea
May	Emerald	Lily of the Valley
June	Pearl	Rose
July	Ruby	Larkspur
August	Peridot	Gladiolus
September	Sapphire	Aster
October	Opal	Calendula
November	Topaz	Chrysanthemum
December	Turquoise	Narcissus

Name	Date	Ideas	Bought	Cost

ANNIVERSARY & BIRTHDAY GIFT RECORD

Name	Date	Ideas	Bought	Cost

Exercise for fun

A large dose of the feel-good factor never goes amiss and one
quick way to access it is to get moving. What better motivation
is there to maintain suppleness and fitness levels than to have
a fabulous time while you're doing it? Give it a try!

When it comes to exercise, everyone has their likes and dislikes so choosing the right class is essential. There are plenty available and chances are at least one will suit you. Why not give several a try? You may be surprised. Your respiratory system, cardiovascular fitness and muscle tone will be all the better for it, and you're sure to come out smiling because all that exercise releases endorphins, the happy hormones.

Aerobics, body sculpt or legs, bums and tums do it for some people. Yoga, Pilates and tai chi are all excellent and self-absorbing, improving focus,

balance and posture. Classes in the swimming pool help to build strength while putting less strain on your joints since the water provides both resistance and support.

You can get rid of a lot of pent-up emotion, and lose weight, with boxing training, but if letting rip in a less aggressive way is your main enjoyment factor, think about the pleasures of moving to music. Even if clubbing is out of the question, dancing isn't! It's fun and sociable, and while you're gyrating as energetically as you like, you're getting a seriously good workout.

DANCE, DANCE, DANCE

The trend of combining dance and exercise has caught on in a big way. Getting fit has never been so much fun. Find a Clubbercise class near you and see if you agree. Luminous glow sticks at the ready, cue music and away you go. If you're not fit before you go, you soon will be. There probably is a routine but under dim disco lighting, no one can see if a shape or two turns out not quite as expected.

Zumba is another where you follow an instructor as best as you can, this time to fast moving Latin rhythms.

For fans of the music of 1930s and '40s America, swing is the one, made even better if you dress in style – swirly skirt at the ready. Swingtrain classes are billed as 'high-intensity dance cardio workouts', but they add 'suitable for all levels of fitness' – and everyone has got to start somewhere!

Swing evolved into jive and ceroc and although you need a partner for these, you may well find one at the class since it's not unusual for people to go on their own.

You definitely need a partner for salsa, which is a mixture of Afro-Caribbean and Latin styles and as flirtatious as you would like it to be.

Tap, line and ballroom dancing are all more structured – you have to concentrate so your co-ordination skills get a workout, too – and if you fancy something really different, give belly dancing a go, especially good for toning deep core, pelvic and hip muscles, or Bollywood style, blending classical Indian dance with hip hop and jazz.

So why not give it a whirl and find out what fun this exercise business really can be? Check websites for classes and availability near you.

The trend of combining dance and exercise has caught on in a big way

PRIVATE WORKOUT

If you can't make a class, or prefer not to, there's no need to miss out. Through the NHS website (NHS Fitness Studio) you can access videos of various exercise workouts, including La Bomba (which is a combination of dance moves set to Latin American dance music, hip hop, Afrobeats and R&B), and belly dancing for beginners. Try them out in the privacy of your own home. Invite friends round to join in, have a party and laugh yourself fit!

WEBSITES

areyoudancing.com
dancenearyou.co.uk
exercisemovedance.org
jazzercise.co.uk
nhs.uk
swingtrain.com

L'ive more with less

Apart from a calm and clean home, decluttering has many life-enhancing advantages including more cash to spend on experiences rather than 'stuff' and a happier state of mind free of the compulsion to purchase more.

How should you declutter? Tackle an area of one room at a time. Hold each item you find and ask yourself, 'Do I love it or is it useful?' If the answer is no then it should go. Take a look at the tips opposite on recycling and selling. Sort items into different boxes, each labelled with its destination e.g. charity shop, car boot sale etc. Don't try to declutter the whole house at once. Plan it in your diary, allocating time to each room, and give yourself a break in-between; otherwise you may just become demotivated by the whole process.

Now, how do you keep all that space clutter-free? It's really an attitude of mind. Bask in your new-found space and freedom from 'stuff'. Happiness lies in 'doing' rather than 'having', accumulating experiences rather than things.

Spend the cash you've earned from selling or saved on spending on a great day out with family, or save it for a special holiday.

Another upside of living with less is that house cleaning becomes quicker and easier, so as well as cash, you have more time to devote to having fun.

PRESERVE YOUR SPACE

- Think 'green'. Production of goods requires a lot of energy and by buying less you're being kinder to the environment. And also less packaging will end up in landfill.
- Impulse buying and 24-hour online shopping are complete no-nos. Be selective and go for quality over quantity. Apply the 'do I really need it?' test.
- Abide by the rule of one in, one out (or two out, if possible). That's easy if you're replacing something that's worn out, but try to apply it to all your purchases.
- Comparing yourself with others is a real trap. Only you know what you really want and need to keep you and your family happy.
- Keep a charity box and take it to the shop every few weeks. Tap into the feel-good factor of supporting worthwhile causes.
- Enjoy your home: take a few moments to appreciate how it looks – the breathing space and airiness you've created – encourage yourself to keep up the good work. Be vigilant for clutter creep!

'STUFF' DISPOSAL

For information on where and how to recycle absolutely anything, check Recycle Now, the national recycling campaign, which is supported and funded by government with the aim of helping people to recycle more things, more often. If you can keep your stuff out of landfill, that's got to be a good thing.

- The Freecycle group is a useful forum for swapping useable goods and Freegle puts local people in touch with each other on a give or take basis.
- Some charity shops accept clothing in good condition only; others accept worn-out items as well, which they can sell on to be reprocessed into something else. Check first. Many M&S stores have a 'shwopping' bin where you can leave clothes (not necessarily from M&S) to

Bask in your new-found space and freedom from 'stuff'

be passed on to Oxfam.
- To sell designer label clothes and accessories, go to one of the specialist online sites, such as Vinted.
- Take your old spectacles back to the opticians to be sent to Vision Aid.
- Take old batteries to the supermarket – shops selling more than 32kg of batteries per year are obliged to provide battery recycling facilities.
- As well as via eBay and Etsy, you can sell most items on your discard pile through classified ads on Preloved and Gumtree, or through Cash Converters, who have high-street shops as well as operating online.
- To dispose of games, phones and all things electronic, try CeX (Complete Entertainment Exchange) – high-street shops or website. Ensure personal data is removed before parting with phones or computers.
- Sell CDs, DVDs and books online via Music Magpie.
- A car boot sale may be a good idea if you have a lot of things to sell.

FURNITURE REMOVAL

If a piece of furniture has become surplus to requirements but is still in good condition, try the Furniture Re-use Network, which co-ordinates some 300 organisations that collect the goods – electrical, too, in working order – and pass them on to those in need. Otherwise, look for a local organisation that operates in a similar way. The British Heart Foundation collects for free.

WEBSITES

bhf.org.uk
freecycle.org
frn.org.uk
ilovefreegle.org
oxfam.org.uk
recyclenow.com
uk.webuy.com

Recipes & tips online

Whether you're stuck for ideas, hanker after new recipes
or need a hand with the laundry, we are here to help.

The Dairy Diary has long been the source of excellent, innovative and, above all, delicious food ideas together with recipes that are both practical and easy to make, and that proud tradition is reflected in our website.

That's where you'll find heaps of information and advice on all things kitchen and culinary.

SEARCH FOR RECIPES BY INGREDIENTS

For example, the handy 'find' function allows you to search the huge database of recipes by ingredient or recipe title. You can be transported to sections on salads, soups or stews, to wonderful vegetarian dishes and to delightful ideas for what to do with fish.

Recipes for mouth-watering puddings, homely bakes and decadent cakes are there for the asking.

The section on menu suggestions covers all sorts of eventualities from relaxed lunches with friends to more formal evening dinner parties, from children's birthday parties to afternoon tea with friends, and includes cosy nights in for one or two.

SEASONAL RECIPE COLLECTIONS

Appetites and tastes change with the seasons, so that's another route to finding what you're after – try looking under spring, summer, autumn or winter and you will be delighted with the choice available.

Christmas, Easter and Halloween searches will yield delicious recipes to put a smile on the faces of friends and family at these festive times. All triple-tested, of course!

DAIRY DIARY.CO.UK

COOK'S TIPS & TRICKS

Simple things can often make a big difference, and browsing this section will always turn up some new tricks to try.

HOME & LAUNDRY

Of course, there's much more than cookery on offer on the Dairy Diary website. Practical advice on home management and laundry feature, too.

When it comes to laundry, there's not much to it, right? You sort by colour and fabric type, check the care labels, load the washing machine (loosely) and hey presto!

Well, yes, but if you follow the tips on our website, you may get better results.

WIN, WIN, WIN!

While you're visiting us online, why not enter one of our regular competitions?

The prizes are terrific and you never know – as someone once said, you've got to be in it to win it!

Subscribe to our regular newsletters and you'll never miss out again!

FIND MORE TIPS LIKE THIS AT DAIRYDIARY.CO.UK

HOW TO STORE BERRIES

Fresh berries will last longer if you rinse them in water (10 parts) mixed with vinegar (1 part).

STAINLESS STEEL

Surgical spirit will remove spots from stainless steel. Fizzy soda water is also a good cleaner.

HOW TO STORE HERBS

Store ready cut herbs inside a bottle of olive oil – it preserves the herbs for later use and flavours the oil.

SPILLAGE ON A CARPET

Pour a pint of water over the stain as soon as possible, cover with old towels and leave for two hours.

SPEEDY SNIPPING

Instead of a knife use kitchen scissors to cut herbs, pizza, fish or meat. Always wash well afterwards.

FLUFFY TOWELS

Everyone likes soft towels, but don't use fabric conditioner – it makes them less absorbent.

HOW TO STORE ONIONS

Store onions in a brown paper bag to stop them sprouting or going mouldy. Allow some air in.

DAIRYDIARY.CO.UK
FOR RECIPES, TIPS & LOTS MORE

TOO SPICY, TOO HOT?

If you've got carried away with the chilli and spices, squeeze the juice of a couple of limes into the pot.

WASHING MACHINE

Regularly run empty at a high temperature to clear out greasy residues and kill off any lurking bacteria.

WHEN TO ADD HERBS

Add chives and leafy herbs such as basil and coriander towards the end of cooking to preserve the flavour.

WASHING BY HAND

It's safer to squeeze rather than wring, especially wool and silk. Roll in a clean white towel and squeeze gently.

KEEP UP WITH THE LATEST NEWS

Catch up with the latest happenings at Dairy Diary on our blog dairydiarychat.co.uk. You'll discover what's new, find top tips on all sorts of subjects, be inspired by arts and crafts and try brand new recipes before they're even in print!

You can also find us on
- Facebook
- Twitter
- Instagram
- Pinterest
- YouTube

Garden tricks

Seeing is believing but can you believe what you see? Whatever the size or shape of your garden, make the most of it by cultivating a few illusions along with your herbaceous borders; and on a practical level, a few other little tricks can help, too.

'Oh what a tangled web we weave when first we practise to deceive.'

Well, when it comes to the garden, let's not get too involved in Shakespeare's tangled web, but practising to deceive, that's another matter. You might think a straightforward rectangular plot is destined to be boring forever, but not so.

The eye can be fooled more easily than you may think. If your precious plot falls a tad short of your dreams by being too small, too narrow or just too dull, wising up to a trick or two may make all the difference.

SHAPES

How you treat open spaces is one crucial aspect of making the garden appear other than it actually is. A circular lawn, for example, is a good ruse to make a small garden appear to be bigger than its square

footage. Two overlapping circles are even better, the bigger one nearer the house to lengthen the garden and vice versa to shorten it.

If you can lead the eye up the garden path, in more ways than one, that will help your false perspective plan, too. A straight path that tapers slightly as it progresses away from the house elongates the garden, while a zigzag widens it. Snake a track around your patch, and use paving slabs at jaunty angles as stepping stones, to make the whole garden seem bigger.

Another optical trick is to divide the garden, even a small one, so you can't see it all at once. Extend the flowerbed into the lawn or have a short row of pots with flowers and shrubs to do the job. Bamboos and ornamental grasses make interesting screens, as do trellises and archways covered in roses or clematis, or jasmine or honeysuckle, or runner beans. If space is not an issue, you could have a designated kitchen garden, play area, rock garden – whatever your special interest may be.

COLOURS

The rule of thumb is that pale colours appear to be farther away than bright ones, so if bigger is the aim, have vibrantly coloured plants near the house and paler, subtler ones farther away. A back fence stained pale grey or green sends it away, and to enhance the

effect, you could position a delicate focal point in front of it, such as a planter or a small garden table and two chairs. It's better to avoid having tall or spreading trees or shrubs at the end of the garden because a heavily shaded area there will foreshorten the perspective.

HELPFUL HINTS

- For a quick and easy way to keep your flowerbeds going through the season, sink plastic flowerpots in the earth and drop in your plants still in their garden-centre pots. You can change them as you wish.
- Vegetable cooking water is full of nutrients and, once cooled, your plants will love it.
- A couple of times a month, distribute used tea or coffee grounds around acid-loving plants, such as azaleas and camellias, to keep the pH of the soil acidic.
- Epsom salts are a gardener's friend because of their high magnesium and sulphate content. For tomatoes and peppers, pop a tablespoon in with the soil when planting, then sprinkle around the growing plants. For containers, add a couple of tablespoons to the watering can once or twice a month.
- Use gravel as mulch around drought-tolerant plants, which need good drainage e.g. sedums and other succulents, and alpines.
- Plant thyme between stepping stones or in cracked crazy paving for a beautiful aroma when trodden on. If you prefer your paved areas to be plant-free underfoot, use mortar in the cracks rather than sand, which encourages seeds to germinate.

Pale colours appear to be farther away than bright ones

- To ensure watering continues even when you're elsewhere, on holiday for instance, make a lot of holes in plastic water bottles, bury them next to the plants in question (top above ground) and fill with water. The water will seep out as the soil dries, and it will reach deep roots rather than surface weeds.
- Install a water butt if you can, and don't forget to use it – plants much prefer rainwater to the treated variety from a tap.
- Use a permanent marker pen to write plant names on an upturned flowerpot or a stone rather than on a lolly-stick marker because that either goes missing or looks tatty in no time.
- Never lose the run of your garden twine – keep it in an upturned flowerpot with the end poking out of the drainage hole in the bottom.
- Keep a small bed of nettles to encourage ladybirds, which eat aphids. Should any aphids escape to colonize your roses or runner beans, zap them with a solution of washing-up liquid.
- Scrunch up eggshells before composting or they will survive to adorn your flowerbeds.
- Don't forget to turn the compost to allow air to circulate – ideally once a month – and to keep it moist in dry weather. If the compost is smelly and slimy, add more woody material, cardboard or straw. If it's dry and doesn't seem to be rotting, add more greenery, such as grass clippings, or try a commercial activator. If the compost bin turns into a breeding ground for flies, too much moisture and not enough air are likely to be to blame. Add more woody material and turn, and remember to put garden waste on top of kitchen waste to counteract the problem.

WEEDS

For some people, weeding is therapeutic and satisfying; for others, it's not so appealing, in which case, consider ground-cover plants. Mats of foliage and flowers spreading around trees and shrubs save hours of weeding not to mention backache. Ground-cover geraniums and roses, *Vinca minor*, *Alchemilla mollis* and *Bergenia purpurascens* are all attractive options.

Mulch is an effective weed suppressant because light cannot penetrate through it, so stopping the seeds from germinating. Clear weeds first, then spread the mulch over the whole bed and top up each spring. Organic mulches, such as compost, bark and leafmould, are also soil improvers since they gradually rot down. They should be laid to a depth of 10cm (4in);

others, such as gravel, stone chippings or pebbles, to a depth of 2.5-5cm (1-2in).

Alternatively, if you just want to kill the blighters but commercial chemicals are off the agenda, pour boiling water on them and excavate with a sharp knife or trowel – or buy an organic weedkiller, although these may not kill the roots. Be careful to avoid plants you don't want to affect.

Flower & foodie fairs

Coming to a town or village near you – a long-awaited spring fair, followed by a summer festival and probably an autumn show. When spring is in the air and everyone is longing to be reminded of what sunshine feels like, a flower or garden show can prove irresistibly attractive – and food is never off the agenda.

Flowers, gardens, food – a day featuring any or all of these presents a mouth-watering prospect. A trip to a county show or country fair makes a wonderful day out but if you prefer an event where the emphasis is on growing – and/ or perhaps sampling local produce – a more specialist show may be the answer.

There's no shortage of them, big and small, whatever your interest may be.

GARDEN INSPIRATION

Great ideas will be on display whatever the size of the show.

Inspiration may dawn whether you're at Hampton Court or a village fête in Yorkshire.

There's no denying, though, that the bigger shows have a certain pizzazz. Chelsea is probably the best-known flower show, but if that's not for you – or you don't want to wait until late May – Harrogate in April has got pretty much everything, including show gardens, community plots, kitchen gardens and nurseries, as has the Flower Show Cardiff (also in April) and the Malvern Spring Festival (pre-Chelsea May). There are autumn shows

at Harrogate and Malvern, too, in September. It's usually a good idea to buy tickets in advance, so plan ahead.

On the other hand, local shows don't involve time-consuming travelling, so may be more relaxing than venturing farther afield.

In the summer months, you're spoilt for choice. Towns and cities across the land from Shrewsbury to Taunton, Southport to St Helier, hold wonderfully colourful and entertaining events, each with their own take on what can legitimately be included under the name flower show – vintage car rides, arts and crafts stalls, various competitions.

For something a bit different, look out for the National Garden Schemes weekend in June when private gardeners throw open their gates and welcome you in to inspect their carefully tended plots. Money raised goes to various charities.

A SPECIAL FLOWER

A venue full of different varieties of your favourite bloom is a glorious idea. If orchids have stolen your heart, for instance, Kew Gardens is the place, or London for the RHS Spring Plant and Orchid Show; if it's camellias, head to Chiswick House, also in London. February/March is the time. For roses – and who doesn't love roses? – RHS Rosemoor, Devon, beckons in June, but there are fragrant displays in gardens all over the country, including Coughton Court in Warwickshire and Alnwick in Northumberland.

The Gardens of the Rose in St Albans, Hertfordshire, home of the Royal National Rose Society, are open for the summer only. If it's a serious rosefest you want, that's the place to go.

SNOWDROPS

Shows devoted to a particular species, from daffodils to dahlias, are often put on by the national or local society – or just because. Look at Shaftesbury. Come February the whole place is awash with snowdrops. The townsfolk began planting them to celebrate the Queen's Diamond Jubilee in 2012 and they've been planting them ever since. Now the Shaftesbury Snowdrop Festival offers designated walks, a heritage collection, exhibitions of snowdrop-themed arts and crafts and a splendid grand finale featuring a snowdrop lantern parade. Snowdrop heaven and all a bit special!

FOODIE HEAVEN

To judge from the number of dedicated food festivals on offer in the UK, anyone would think that eating is a national pastime to rival gardening! From Liverpool to Leamington, an appetite-teaser will be on offer near you at some point during the year, practically guaranteed. On top of that, every show, fair or festival has its food stands, often featuring local produce to eat there or takeaway. Best advice? Don't eat beforehand!

For cheese lovers especially, the news is all good. As well as featuring in practically every food festival going, cheese is the flavour of the month in April in Melton Mowbray where the Artisan Cheese Fair has folk flocking, while at Nantwich in July you can judge for yourself at the International Cheese Awards.

If you've a taste for the sea, the Lowestoft fish fayre (June) or the Whitstable oyster fair (July) may float your boat, and if fruit is your thing, head to Brogdale, near Faversham in Kent – in June for the strawberry fair, July for the cherry fair and August-October for plum and apple festivals. Aldeburgh Festival has a bit of everything!

At some point in the year, chances are you'll find a Chilli Fiesta near you, where you can eat, drink and shop for all things chilli related. Go for the experience – you can always have an ice cream if things get too hot! You could make that a garlic ice cream – surprisingly delicious – if you visit the Garlic Festival, held in August at the world's foremost producers of the delectable bulbs – the Garlic Farm on the Isle of Wight.

SMARTEN UP!

The fairs and festivals habit has been fully embraced by some rather grand venues. Various stately homes and mansions, not to mention the odd castle, are getting in on the act. So if you fancy pursuing your interest in impressive as well as convivial surroundings, Blenheim Palace in Oxfordshire has a food festival in May and a flower show in June; Sandringham, Norfolk, puts on a flower show in July and a food and drink festival in August; and Leeds Castle in Kent stages the Chelsea Fringe, full of 'horticultural happenings' in late May/early June as well as a festival of flowers in September. Arundel Castle in West Sussex puts on an annual tulip festival in April/May. Woburn Abbey Garden Show, Holker Hall and Gardens Festival and Chatsworth's Flower Show are all in June, while Hever in Bloom at Hever Castle, Kent, Anne Boleyn's old stamping ground, is in July.

THE GREAT BRITISH FOOD FESTIVAL

If food, glorious food is the main event for you, look out for events cropping up under this banner throughout the spring, summer and autumn.

Artisan producers set out their stalls, around 100 of them, full of favourite goodies and delectable treats.

Locations usually include:

- Stonyhurst College, Lancashire (April)
- Hardwick Hall, Derbyshire (April/May)
- Harewood House, Leeds (May)
- Weston Park, Staffordshire (May)
- Kelmarsh Hall, Northamptonshire (July)
- Knebworth House, Hertfordshire (July)
- Castle Howard, York (July) (also holds a flower festival in June/July)
- Bowood House, Wiltshire (August)
- Arley Hall, Cheshire (September)

WEBSITES

aldeburghfoodanddrink.co.uk
brogdalecollections.org
chillifest.net
chilliworld.com
garlicfestival.co.uk
greatbritishfoodfestival.com
mrs.org.uk
ngs.org.uk
visitengland.co.uk
visitkent.co.uk

Check all venues for dates, times and facilities before you visit.

Cheese, glorious cheese!

Cheese is one of the oldest foods known to mankind. Whoever hit upon a way to turn perishable milk into storable cheese – thousands of years ago and probably by accident – deserves a medal! Nowadays, locally produced varieties are more popular than ever and British cheesemakers are among the best in the world.

Rollright, Hafod, Lord of the Hundreds, Winslade, Perl Las – not to mention Barwheys, Berkswell and Baron Bigod – a cheese by any other name tastes just as good! The creative talent that goes into making fabulous cheeses is matched by the imagination that goes into deciding what to call them!

Over 700 named cheeses are produced in the UK, which is remarkable when you think that up until rationing stopped in 1954 it was more or less Cheddar or nothing. That didn't mean the cheese-eating public weren't interested, though, as recognised in 1982 by the manufacturers of Lymeswold, the first new English cheese in 200 years. Then, in the 1990s, with the price of milk declining, dairy farmers who felt the need to diversify said 'Cheese!' and ended up smiling.

Many a small enterprise started up, often with just a few cows or goats or sheep, the owners expanding the herd and/or buying in milk from carefully selected sources as their cheeses found favour; and longer established cheese specialists, such as Lyburn on the edge of the New Forest, found themselves ahead of the game. Roger and Liz Sutton started the Delamere Dairy, in the depths of Cheshire's Delamere Forest, with just three goats in 1985. Now their cheeses are sold all over the UK. The momentum continues, which for cheese addicts is all to the good.

SHOP LOCAL

This cheesy renaissance means that we can easily try unusual varieties produced by local farms and cheesemakers, who sometimes follow old-fashioned recipes and are sometimes more experimental and innovative. Local cheeses are often handmade and so slight variations occur from batch to batch, adding to the sense of trying something really different.

What about Drunken Burt, rind-washed in cider, one of Cheshire-based Claire Burt's half a dozen handmade cheeses; or Lord of the Hundreds from the Traditional Cheese Dairy in East Sussex, often used as an alternative to Parmesan.

The Appleby Creamery in Cumbria's Eden Valley, sends hard, soft and blue cheeses from goats' and ewes' milk all over the Lake District and into Scotland, while in the deepest Cotswolds Good Queen Maude reigns supreme, courtesy of Alex James and Elaine Foran, who also offer us several other flavoursome cheeses you won't find elsewhere.

If you can't get to these places and your local deli doesn't stock what you want, you can always buy online from the makers or a good cheesemonger.

CURDS AND WHEY

On the face of it, the cheese-making process is quite straightforward and can be summed up as curdling, draining, pressing, ripening, but, of course, it's not as simple as that. The skill lies in the detail. A whole swathe of modifications has evolved over time and by region, and with today's proliferation of artisanal cheesemakers, the variety of cheeses available is enormous.

A live starter culture is added to milk to turn it sour and then a coagulating agent, usually some form of rennet (but sometimes lemon juice and/or vinegar), to turn it into a soft substance known as curds. Once the curds have set, they are cut to release the liquid (whey), and piled on top of each other to squeeze out even more whey. Then the curds are cut into small pieces (milled) and salt is added before they are pressed into moulds and stored until ready (depending on the cheese).

Salt is necessary to inhibit growth of bacteria in the starter culture, to control water content, to add texture and as a preservative. In low-fat varieties, less salt can result in a stronger smell, so reducing both salt and fat can be challenging for the cheesemaker.

Far from being just water, whey contains plenty of nutrients and can be made into soft cheeses, such as ricotta. It can also be made into whey protein and whey powder, which is of interest to some gym-goers to help build muscle.

WHAT CHEESE?

Cheese can be categorized in several ways – soft, semi soft, medium hard, hard; using milk from cows, sheep or goats; or whether it looks mouldy or not, in the tastiest possible way! Blue cheeses have either been skewered to encourage mould to grow or injected with a form of Penicillium.

Some soft-ripened cheeses, such as Brie and Camembert, develop a white crust as the result of exposure to mould. Other soft cheeses may be periodically soaked in brine, beer, wine or brandy, which firms up and colours the rind and may encourage a strong smell. Think Stinking Bishop, made in Gloucestershire by Charles Martell.

Then there are the fresh cheeses, the simplest of all. Milk is curdled and drained and not much else happens. These include cottage cheese, paneer, curd (quark), mascarpone and other cream cheeses – soft, mild and with a short shelf life.

Mozzarella, made by stretching and kneading curds in hot water to form a ball, is usually kept in brine, but not for too long.

CHEESEMONGERS

Once the cheese is made it has to be nurtured. Should it be turned, washed, brushed, left alone? For how long? Should it be stored in wood, straw, paper, wrapped in ash? At what temperature? And what about humidity?

Who'd have thought the ripening process could be so complicated! Affinage, as it's known in the business, is a delicate science and the affineur has to take all sorts of things into account, including when the milk was produced and what the animals have eaten, as well as how the cheese has been made and how to keep friendly bacteria happy. The whole point is to develop or enhance texture, flavour and aroma, enough to make all confirmed foodies drool and to satisfy the taste buds of the most discerning cheese lover.

Although many local cheesemakers undertake the ripening process themselves, others send their cheeses to cheesemongers who have maturing rooms and cellars. These specialists do the necessary before selling the wondrous results to an eagerly awaiting public. Take a trip to a good cheesemonger's and you'll soon be lost in admiration of the fine skill, and variety of cheeses, on display.

Paxton & Whitfield is the daddy of them all, having been plying its trade for over 200 years, but Neal's Yard Dairy, La Fromagerie and Buchanan's in London, the Courtyard Dairy in Yorkshire and the Fine Cheese Company in Bath also draw cheese-loving crowds.

Many cheesemongers, whether or not they offer affinage, have cafés, events, talks and tastings. If you find yourself in Keswick in the Lake District, seek out Cartmel Cheeses and be amazed at all the cheesy treats on offer. And as far as online only goes, don't neglect the wonderfully named Pong Cheese – irresistible!

WEBSITES

cheeseboard.co.uk
greatbritishchefs.com
pongcheese.co.uk
specialistcheesemakers.co.uk
thecourtyarddairy.co.uk

Choose cheese

GOAT'S CHEESE SOUFFLÉS WITH A WALNUT SALAD

Serves 4 • Time 45 mins • Calories 520
Fat 42.9g (19.6g saturated)

Butter 75g (3oz)
Parmesan or vegetarian alternative
50g (2oz), finely grated
Plain flour 50g (2oz)
Full fat milk 300ml (½ pint)
Rindless goat's cheese 100g (3½oz),
broken into pieces
Eggs 4, separated
Ground nutmeg a couple of generous
pinches
Mixed salad leaves 50g (2oz), such as
watercress, baby spinach and rocket
Walnut pieces 25g (1oz)
Olive oil 2 tbsp
Lime 1, juice only

1 Melt 25g (1oz) of the butter and use it to grease four 200ml (7fl oz) soufflé dishes. Then sprinkle with some of the Parmesan-style cheese. This gives the soufflés something to stick to as they rise. Set the dishes on a baking sheet.
2 Melt the remaining butter in a large saucepan, add the flour and mix well. Remove the pan from the heat and gradually add the milk, whisking well after each addition. Then return the pan to the heat and bring the sauce to the boil, whisking all the time. Continue cooking for about 1 minute, still whisking, until you have a smooth thick sauce. Remove the pan from the heat and leave to cool for 10 minutes. Preheat the oven to 200°C/180°fan/Gas 6.
3 Beat in the goat's cheese and remaining Parmesan-style cheese. Then beat in the egg yolks. Season with salt, pepper and nutmeg.
4 Whisk the egg whites with an electric hand whisk until they form stiff peaks. Fold one-third into the cheese sauce with a metal spoon, then gently fold in the rest. Spoon the mix into the prepared dishes and bake for 15–20 minutes or until golden and well risen.
5 Drizzle the salad and walnuts with oil and lime juice and serve as soon as the soufflés come out of the oven.

EASY CHEESY SOUFFLÉ OMELETTE

Serves 2 • Time 15-18 mins • Calories 351
Fat 29g (12.2g saturated)

Eggs 4
Snipped chives 2 tbsp
Camembert cheese 110g (4oz), chopped
Sunflower oil 2 tsp
Roasted vegetables to serve (optional)

1 It is easier to make one omelette at a time – unless you are lucky enough to have two smallish non-stick frying pans. Separate two of the eggs into two bowls. Beat the egg yolks with half the chives and season with salt and pepper. Divide the chopped cheese into four portions and stir one of the portions into the egg yolks.

2 Whisk the egg whites with an electric hand whisk until they form stiff peaks, then gently fold into the cheesy egg mix with a metal spoon. Preheat the grill to hot.

3 Heat 1 tsp of the oil in a non-stick frying pan and add the egg mix. Cook until the omelette is just starting to turn golden underneath. Then scatter with another portion of cheese. Pop the pan under the grill and continue cooking until the cheese has melted and the omelette is puffed and only just set.

4 Carefully tip the omelette onto a serving plate, folding it in half as you do so. Repeat with the remaining mix to make the second omelette. Serve with roasted vegetables.

TWO CHEESE AND ONION TART

Serves 3 • Time 40 mins • Calories 614
Fat 41g (20.8g saturated)

Ready-rolled puff pastry 320g pack
Tomato chutney or ketchup 3 tbsp
Onion 1, peeled and thinly sliced
Cheddar cheese, Double Gloucester or Red Leicester mixed with a blue cheese such as **Gorgonzola or Stilton** 150g (5oz), cut into cubes
Baby plum or cherry tomatoes 10, halved
Chopped parsley to garnish (optional)
Green salad to serve (optional)

1 Preheat the oven to 220°C/ 200°C fan/Gas 7. Carefully unroll the pastry and put the sheet (measuring 23 x 35cm/9 x 14in) on to a heavy baking sheet.

2 With a sharp knife, mark a border about 1.5cm (½in) in from the edge all round and lightly mark it for decoration. With a fork, prick inside the border, to keep the pastry flat while it cooks.

3 Spread the chutney or ketchup inside the border, then scatter the onion slices over the sauce, followed by the cheese cubes and tomato halves. Season with black pepper.

4 Bake the tart in the bottom half of the oven for about 30 minutes until the pastry is browned and crispy. Cool for a few minutes and then sprinkle with a little parsley. Serve the tart warm or cold with a crisp green salad, if you like.

Cook's information

DRY WEIGHT CONVERSIONS

grams (g)	ounces (oz)
15	½
25	1
50	2
75	3
110	4 (¼lb)
150	5
175	6
200	7
225	8 (½lb)
250	9
275	10
300	11
350	12 (¾lb)
375	13
400	14
425	15
450	16 (1lb)
500	1lb 2oz
680	1½lb
750	1lb 10oz
900	2lb

These quantities are not exact, but they have been calculated to give proportionately correct measurements.

LIQUID CONVERSIONS

millilitres (ml)	fluid ounces (fl oz)	US cups
15	½	1 tbsp (level)
30	1	⅛
60	2	¼
90	3	⅜
125	4	½
150	5 (¼ pint)	⅔
175	6	¾
225	8	1
300	10 (½ pint)	1¼
350	12	1½
450	16	2
500	18	2¼
600	20 (1 pint)	2½
900	1½ pints	3¾
1 litre	1¾ pints	1 quart (4 cups)
1.25 litres	2 pints	1¼ quarts
1.5 litres	2½ pints	3 US pints
2 litres	3½ pints	2 quarts

These quantities are not exact, but they have been calculated to give proportionately correct measurements.

SPOON MEASURES

1 tablespoon	=	3 level teaspoons
1 level tablespoon	=	15ml
1 level teaspoon	=	5ml
If greater accuracy is not required:		
1 rounded teaspoon	=	2 level teaspoons
1 heaped teaspoon	=	3 level teaspoons or 1 level tablespoon

REFERENCE INTAKE (RI)

Energy (calories)	2,000
Fat (g)	70
of which saturates (g)	20
Carbohydrate (g)	260
of which total sugars (g)	90
Protein (g)	50
Salt (g)	6

These amounts indicate an adult's daily requirements for a healthy, balanced diet.

GRILLING TIMES: FISH

	minutes each side
Cod (steak)	5–6
Dover sole (fillet)	2–3
Halibut (steak)	5–6
Herring (whole)	4–5
Mackerel (whole)	6–7
Monkfish (steak)	5–6
Plaice (whole)	4–6
Plaice (fillet)	2–3
Salmon (steak)	5–6
Skate	5–6
Tuna (steak)	1–2

Times given for fish weighing approximately 175–225g (6–8oz).

OVEN TEMPERATURES

°C	(fan)	°F	gas	description
110	(90)	225	¼	cool
120/130	(100/110)	250	½	cool
140	(120)	275	1	very low
150	(130)	300	2	very low
160/170	(140/150)	325	3	low to moderate
180	(160)	350	4	moderate
190	(170)	375	5	moderately hot
200	(180)	400	6	hot
220	(200)	425	7	hot
230	(210)	450	8	hot
240	(220)	475	9	very hot

Guide to recommended equivalent settings, not exact conversions. Always refer to your cooker instruction book.

ROASTING TIMES: MEAT*

Set oven temperature to 180°C/160°fan/Gas 4.

	cooking time per 450g/1lb	extra cooking time
Beef		
rare	20 min	20 min
medium	25 min	25 min
well done	30 min	30 min
Lamb		
medium	25 min	25 min
well done	30 min	30 min
Pork		
medium	30 min	30 min
well done	35 min	35 min

Let the cooked meat rest for 5–15 minutes before carving to allow the juices to be reabsorbed and to make carving easier.

STEAMING TIMES: VEGETABLES

	minutes
Asparagus	5–7
Beansprouts	3–4
Beetroot (sliced)	5–7
Broccoli (florets)	5–7
Brussels sprouts	5–7
Cabbage (chopped)	4–6
Carrots (thickly sliced)	5–7
Cauliflower (florets)	5–7
Courgettes (sliced)	3–5
Green beans	5–7
Leeks	5–8
Mangetout peas	3–5
Peas	3–5
Potatoes (cubed)	5–7

Times given are for steaming from when water has started to boil.

ROASTING TIMES: POULTRY*

	oven temperature	cooking time per 450g/1lb	extra cooking time	resting time
Chicken	220°C/200°fan/Gas 7 for 20 min; then 190°C/170°fan/Gas 5	20 min	20 min	15 min
Turkey (stuffed weight)	220°C/200°fan/Gas 7 uncovered, for 30 min; then, covered, 190°C/170°fan/Gas 5; then for last 30 min, uncovered, 200°C/180°fan/Gas 6	18 min	18 min	30 min
Duck	230°C/210°fan/Gas 8 for 20 min; then 180°C/160°fan/Gas 4	15 min	—	15 min

* Note that for fan ovens, cooking times are generally reduced by 10 minutes for every hour. These timings and oven temperatures are guidelines – follow instructions on packaging if possible.

Stain removal

The most important factor in attacking stains is to act swiftly. The newer the stain, whether greasy or non-greasy, or a combination of the two, the easier it will be to remove without damage. Always check care labels, if you can, and do what they say.

First and foremost, check what processes and cleaning agents are suitable for the stained item. Wool and silk often need to be treated differently from cotton and synthetics, for example.

Likewise, bear in mind that whites may need to be treated differently from coloureds. In any case, always check for colourfastness before soaking.

Biological detergent works well even at low temperatures due to the enzymes it contains. Whenever you can, use it for stain removal but don't use it, or any other enzyme-based cleaner, on wool or silk. For hand-washing, old or delicate fabrics and baby clothes, use a mild non-biological detergent.

PERSONAL

Blood: Soak in cold water with biological detergent or salt; or rub in a paste of bicarb and cold water, leave to dry, brush off.

Wash in biological detergent (if possible).
Make-up: Work in biological liquid detergent; wash as usual.
Perspiration: Sponge with white vinegar, rinse and soak in salt solution or biological detergent. Soften old stains with glycerine. Rinse, wash as usual.
Urine: Rinse in cold water; dab with hydrogen peroxide (see below), or soak in biological detergent; rinse, wash as usual.
Vomit: Rinse under running cold water; soak in a sterilising solution, or biological detergent with some disinfectant added; wash as usual.

FOOD AND DRINKS

Chocolate: Rinse in cold water; apply biological liquid detergent and soak overnight if necessary; wash in suitable detergent.
Coffee: Soak in lukewarm water, use a pre-wash treatment and wash in suitable detergent.

Egg: Sponge with cold salty water and wash in biological detergent (if possible).
Gravy: Soak in biological detergent and cold water; wash as usual.
Grease: Treat with eucalyptus oil, then dampen and rub with washing-up liquid; rinse and wash in biological detergent in water as hot as fabric allows.
Milk and fruit juice: Rinse in cold water, then soak in liquid detergent and wash in water as hot as the fabric allows.
Oil/salad dressings: Blot and dab gently with biological liquid detergent; or sprinkle with bicarb to absorb grease, brush off and soak in washing-up liquid. Wash as usual.
Tea: Soak in lukewarm water, use a pre-wash treatment and wash in heavy-duty detergent; or dab with lemon juice, rinse and wash in biological detergent; or pour white

CLEANING KIT

Bicarbonate of soda: Use this – or cornflour or talcum powder – to absorb grease and oil.
Detergents: Biological/non-biological/heavy-duty/mild. Liquid detergent is good for oily stains and as a pre-wash treatment.
Eucalyptus oil: Available from major chemists. Good for greasy stains.

Glycerine: For treating old stains before washing.
Hydrogen peroxide: Ask your chemist for 3%, which is 10 volume strength (VS). Don't use on wool or silk.
Methylated spirits: From diy stores. Apply with cotton-wool buds. Don't use on fabric that contains acetate or triacetate.
Pre-wash treatments: Some of these are formulated to

treat a whole raft of common stains, some are more specific. Follow the instructions on the container.
White distilled vinegar: Use as a solution of 15ml vinegar to 300ml water (3 tsp to ½ pint); or mixed to a paste with bicarbonate of soda.
White spirit: Available from diy stores. Good for paint and grease.

WHAT TO DO

- Remove any solids with a blunt knife, and blot liquids with white kitchen paper.
- Apply stain remover to a small, unseen area and wait 5–10 minutes. If the fabric reacts, or if in doubt, seek dry-cleaning advice. Avoid treating delicate or expensive fabrics, or those that require dry-cleaning only.
- Don't over-soak the fabric with a cleaning agent. To avoid making a ring mark, use a soft, absorbent cloth to apply the cleaning agent and work in a circular motion from the outside inwards. Dab, rather than rub, because rubbing can damage the fabric and it can also spread the stain.

WEBSITES
dairydiary.co.uk/discover
diynot.com
persil.co.uk
stainexpert.co.uk

vinegar solution over the stain, leave for 10 minutes and wash as usual.

Tomato sauce: Dab gently with biological liquid detergent and wash as usual; or rinse in cold water, dab with white vinegar, rinse and wash as usual.

Wine, red: Pour soda water over the stain, blot, cover with salt and leave for 30 minutes. Soak in cold water; sponge with biological detergent and wash as usual. On upholstery and carpets, cover with salt, leave to absorb and brush off. Dab with warm water and biological detergent; then with cold water.

Wine, white: Rinse in warm water; dab with biological liquid detergent (white vinegar for silk and wool). Rinse and wash as usual. On upholstery and carpets, blot then sponge gently with soapy water (do not rub).

MISCELLANEOUS

Grass: Dab with methylated spirits; rinse with warm soapy water. Use a pre-wash and then wash in heavy-duty detergent.

Ink (ballpoint or felt tip): Dab with methylated spirits; rinse and sponge with biological liquid detergent; wash as usual. If stain persists, treat as rust.

Rust: Dab with lemon juice, cover with salt, leave for at least an hour; rinse and wash as usual.

Suntan lotion: Use a pre-wash for greasy stains, or treat with eucalyptus oil or a product for removing hard-water stains. Wash in biological detergent.

Tar: Treat with eucalyptus oil, then dampen and rub with washing-up liquid; rinse and wash in biological detergent in water as hot as fabric allows.

Washing instructions

TEXTILE CYCLES

Check both the temperature, given by the figure in the tub, and the machine-action, shown by the bar(s) under it. The temperature may be indicated by dots (six for 95°, four for 60°, two for 40° and one for 30°).

 Maximum agitation. Cotton cycle
White cotton or linen articles without special finishes.

 Maximum agitation. Cotton cycle
Cotton or linen articles without special finishes where colours are fast at 60°C.

 Maximum agitation. Cotton cycle
Cotton or linen where colours are fast at 40°C but not at 60°C.

 Medium agitation. Synthetic cycle
Acrylics, acetate or triacetate, including mixtures with wool, polyester and wool blends.

 Minimum agitation. Wool cycle
Wool, including blankets, wool mixed with other fibres, viscose and silk.

 Gentle agitation. Delicates cycle
Silk, acetates and mixed synthetics not colourfast at 40°C.

 Hand wash only
See garment label for further instructions.

 Do not machine or hand wash

DRY-CLEANING

The letter P or F indicates the cleaning fluids that may be used by your professional dry-cleaner.

 May be dry-cleaned

 Do not dry-clean

BLEACHING

 Bleach may be used

 Do not bleach

 Do not use chlorine bleach

DRYING SYMBOLS

Check the label to see if your garment can be tumble-dried; the label may advise using a reduced heat setting by putting a single dot within the circle. Two dots indicate a higher heat setting.

 May be tumble-dried

 Drip dry recommended

 Do not tumble-dry

 Dry flat

 Hang dry

IRONING

- The dots inside the iron indicate the temperature setting. One dot represents the coolest setting and three dots are for the hottest temperature. The table (right) is a guide to the temperature to use for specific types of fabric.
- You should always use the setting recommended by the manufacturer. For some materials the advice may be that you iron on the wrong side of the fabric only, so check the label.
- To avoid creases, store your clothes in drawers and wardrobes loosely; don't pack them in.

 Hot (3 dots)
Cotton, linen and viscose fabrics.

 Warm (2 dots)
Polyester mixtures and wool.

 Cool (1 dot) Acrylic, nylon, acetate, triacetate and polyester.

 Do not iron

Metric conversions

			To convert	multiply by
Length				
1 millimetre (mm)		= 0.0394in	mm to in	0.0394
1 centimetre (cm)	= 10mm	= 0.394in	cm to in	0.394
1 metre (m)	= 100cm	= 1.09yd	m to yd	1.09
1 kilometre (km)	= 1000m	= 0.621 mile	km to mi	0.621
1 inch (in)		= 2.54cm	in to cm	2.54
1 foot (ft)	= 12in	= 30.5cm	ft to cm	30.5
1 yard (yd)	= 3ft	= 0.914m	yd to m	0.914
1 mile (mi)	= 1760yd	= 1.61km	mi to km	1.61
Area				
1 sq millimetre (mm)		= 0.00155sq in	mm^2 to in^2	0.00155
1 sq centimetre (cm)	= 100sq mm	= 0.155sq in	cm^2 to in^2	0.155
1 sq metre (m)	= 10,000sq cm	= 1.2sq yd	m^2 to yd^2	1.2
1 hectare (ha)	= 10,000sq m	= 2.47a	ha to a	2.47
1 sq kilometre (km)	= 100ha	= 0.386sq mile	km^2 to mi^2	0.386
1 sq inch (in)		= 6.45sq cm	in^2 to cm^2	6.45
1 sq foot (ft)	= 144sq in	= 0.0929sq m	ft^2 to m^2	0.0929
1 sq yard (yd)	= 9sq ft	= 0.836sq m	yd^2 to m^2	0.836
1 acre (a)	= 4840sq yd	= 4047sq m	a to m^2	4047
1 sq mile (mi)	= 640a	= 2.59sq km	mi^2 to km^2	2.59
Volume				
1 cu centimetre (cm)	= 1000cu mm	= 0.0611cu in	cm^3 to in^3	0.0611
1 cu decimetre (dm)	= 1000cu cm	= 0.0353cu ft	dm^3 to ft^3	0.0353
1 cu metre (m)	= 1000cu dm	= 1.31cu yd	m^3 to yd^3	1.31
1 cu inch (in)		= 16.4cu cm	in^3 to cm^3	16.4
1 cu foot (ft)	= 1730cu in	= 28.4cu dm	ft^3 to dm^3	28.4
1 cu yard (yd)	= 27cu ft	= 0.765cu m	yd^3 to m^3	0.765
Capacity				
1 millilitre (ml)		= 0.0352fl oz	ml to fl oz	0.0352
1 centilitre (cl)	= 10ml	= 0.352fl oz	cl to fl oz	0.352
1 litre (l)	= 100cl	= 1.76pt	l to pt	1.76
1 fluid ounce (fl oz)		= 28.4ml	fl oz to ml	28.4
1 gill (gi)	= 5fl oz	= 14.2cl	gi to cl	14.2
1 pint (pt)	= 20fl oz	= 0.568l	pt to l	0.568
1 quart (qt)	= 2pt	= 1.14l	qt to l	1.14
1 gallon (gal)	= 4qt	= 4.55l	gal to l	4.55
Weight				
1 gram (g)	= 1000mg	= 0.0353oz	g to oz	0.0353
1 kilogram (kg)	= 1000g	= 2.2lb	kg to lb	2.2
1 tonne (t)	= 1000kg	= 0.984 ton	tonne to ton	0.984
1 ounce (oz)	= 438 grains	= 28.3g	oz to g	28.3
1 pound (lb)	= 16oz	= 0.454kg	lb to kg	0.454
1 stone (st)	= 14lb	= 6.35kg	st to kg	6.35
1 ton (t)	= 160st	= 1.02 tonne	ton to tonne	1.02

Height & weight chart

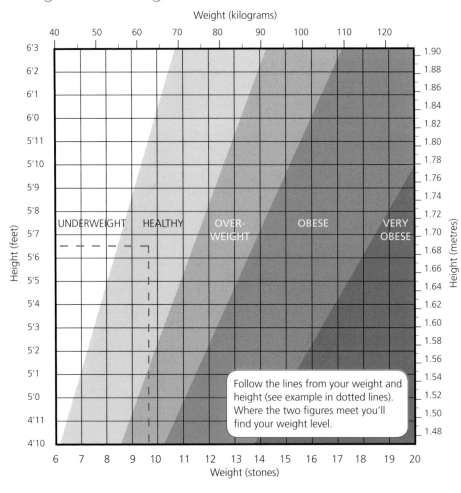

Weight (kilograms)

Height axis (feet): 6'3, 6'2, 6'1, 6'0, 5'11, 5'10, 5'9, 5'8, 5'7, 5'6, 5'5, 5'4, 5'3, 5'2, 5'1, 5'0, 4'11, 4'10

Height axis (metres): 1.90, 1.88, 1.86, 1.84, 1.82, 1.80, 1.78, 1.76, 1.74, 1.72, 1.70, 1.68, 1.66, 1.64, 1.62, 1.60, 1.58, 1.56, 1.54, 1.52, 1.50, 1.48

Chart zones: UNDERWEIGHT, HEALTHY, OVER-WEIGHT, OBESE, VERY OBESE

> Follow the lines from your weight and height (see example in dotted lines). Where the two figures meet you'll find your weight level.

Weight (stones)

GUIDE FOR ADULT MEN AND WOMEN

☐ You may need to see your doctor if you are very underweight.

■ Desirable range for health.

■ Try to lose weight until you are in the desirable range.

■ To avoid potential health problems, it is important to lose weight.

■ Talk to your doctor or practice nurse. You can be referred to a dietitian.

BODY MASS INDEX

To calculate your BMI, divide your weight in kilograms by your height in metres and then divide the answer by your height again. Alternatively, the NHS has an online BMI calculator (nhs.uk).

Below 18.5	underweight	18.5–24.9	healthy
25–29.9	overweight	30 +	obese

2019

31 Monday
New Year's Eve

1 Tuesday JANUARY
New Year's Day
Bank Holiday, UK

2 Wednesday
Bank Holiday, Scotland

3 Thursday

4 Friday

REMINDERS

SPARKLY SLOE GIN JELLIES

Granulated sugar 50g (2oz)
Orange rind 2 broad strips
Gelatine 5 leaves
Sloe gin 175ml (6fl oz)
Sparkling white wine/Prosecco/Cava
350-375ml (12fl oz)
Blueberries and icing sugar to decorate
(optional)

1 Warm sugar in a pan with orange rind
and 150ml (¼ pint) water. Stir until sugar
dissolves. Bring to the boil. Take off heat and
leave for 30 minutes to infuse.

2 Soften gelatine in a bowl of cold water for
5 minutes.

3 Warm orange syrup and remove orange
rind. Squeeze water out of gelatine, add it to
syrup and stir well until dissolved. Pour into
a large jug, stir in sloe gin and leave until
starting to set.

4 Gradually stir in wine and stir every so
often until most of the froth has subsided
and jelly is setting again. Pour into shot
glasses (or cocktail glasses). Chill for 4 hours
or overnight until set. Decorate with fresh
blueberries and a dusting of icing sugar if
you like.

Cook's tip: These jellies are quite boozy and
a small portion is plenty.

Serves 8 • Time 25 mins plus infusion and setting time
Calories 136 • Fibre 0g • Salt 0g • Sugar 13.4g
Fat 0g of which 0g is saturated

JANUARY

7 Monday

8 Tuesday

9 Wednesday

10 Thursday

11 Friday

REMINDERS

Sunday 13

MEDITERRANEAN PASTA BAKE

Pasta shapes 175g (6oz)
Butter 50g (2oz)
Red onion 1, peeled and sliced
Garlic 1 clove, peeled and crushed
Button mushrooms 150g (5oz), wiped and halved
Courgette 1, cut into batons
Baby corn 110g (4oz), halved
Tomato pasta sauce 340/350g jar
Eggs 2
Greek-style plain yogurt 300g (11oz)
Mature Cheddar cheese 150g (5oz), grated
Dried mixed herbs 1 tsp

1 Preheat oven to 200°C/180°fan/Gas 6. Cook pasta according to instructions on packet.
2 Meanwhile, melt butter in a large frying pan and fry onion and garlic for about 5 minutes until softened. Add all remaining vegetables and cook, stirring, for a further 5 minutes.
3 Drain pasta and mix into vegetables with sauce. Transfer to a large buttered ovenproof dish. Beat together eggs, yogurt, cheese, herbs and seasoning and pour over pasta. Bake for 20 minutes until set and golden brown.

Serves 4 • **Time 30 mins**
Calories 655 • Fibre 6.2g • Salt 1.7g • Sugar 0g
Fat 39.5g of which 22.1g is saturated

57

14 Monday
〉 First quarter

15 Tuesday

16 Wednesday

17 Thursday

18 Friday

REMINDERS

Saturday 19

Sunday 20

SPICED GRIDDLED MACKEREL

Mackerel fillets 4 small
Low fat natural yogurt 1 tbsp
Lemon juice 1 tbsp
Root ginger 1cm (½in) piece, peeled and grated
Cayenne pepper 1 tsp
Ground cumin 1 tsp
Garam masala 1 tsp
Olive oil 1 tbsp
Couscous, salad and lemon wedges to serve (optional)

1 Remove any bones from mackerel and slash skins with three diagonal cuts.
2 In a shallow bowl mix together yogurt, lemon juice, ginger and spices with some black pepper. Add fish and rub marinade all over. Cover and set aside for 30 minutes.
3 Oil and heat a non-stick griddle pan. Cook mackerel skin-side up for 3 minutes then turn and cook for another 2 minutes. Serve on a bed of couscous with salad and lemon wedges, if you like.

Serves 2 • Time 25 mins plus marinating
Calories 263 • Fibre 0.3g • Salt 0.4g • Sugar 0g
Fat 20.9g of which 4.1g is saturated

59

21 Monday
○ Full moon

22 Tuesday

23 Wednesday

24 Thursday

25 Friday
Burns' Night

REMINDERS

Sunday 27
(Last quarter

BAKED HAM & EGGS

Ham 4 slices
Crème fraîche 4 tbsp
Tomato 1 large, finely diced
Dried chilli flakes ¼ tsp
Dried mixed herbs ½ tsp
Eggs 4 medium, separated
Paprika for dusting (optional)

1 Preheat oven to 200°C/180°fan/Gas 6 and grease four holes of a muffin tin. Line each of these with ham.
2 In a bowl, mix together crème fraîche, tomatoes, chilli flakes, herbs, egg whites and season to taste. Spoon into ham-lined muffin tin. Make an indent in mixture and spoon egg yolk into each. Season.
3 Bake for 15-18 minutes until egg is cooked. Leave to cool slightly then remove with a palette knife. Serve warm or cold, dusted with paprika, if you like.

Cook's tip: You can use reduced fat crème fraîche, if you prefer. Use up any leftovers for the recipe on page 93.

Serves 4 • Time 30 mins
Calories 162 • Fibre 0.4g • Salt 0.8g • Sugar 0g
Fat 11.6g of which 5.7g is saturated

61

JANUARY

28 Monday

29 Tuesday

30 Wednesday

31 Thursday

1 Friday FEBRUARY

REMINDERS

Sunday 3

LEMON SWIRL BISCUITS

Butter 110g (4oz), softened
Icing sugar 50g (2oz), sifted
Plain flour 125g (4½oz)
Lemon 1, finely grated zest and 1 tsp juice

1 Preheat oven to 160°C/140°fan/Gas 3 and line two baking sheets with baking paper.
2 Cream together butter and sugar. Sift in flour and stir in with lemon zest. Work in lemon juice and mix to a stiff biscuit mix.
3 Spoon mixture into a piping bag fitted with a star nozzle and pipe small swirls onto baking sheets, spaced well apart. When lifting the nozzle from piping each swirl, use a knife to trim the mixture.
4 Bake for 12–15 minutes or until lightly golden and cooked. Leave to cool on baking sheets for about a minute then transfer to a wire rack to cool and firm up. They will keep in an airtight container for a few days.

Makes 12–14 • **Time 25 mins**
Calories 104 • Fibre 0.4g • Salt 0.1g • Sugar 3.6g
Fat 6.6g of which 4.1g is saturated

4 Monday
● New moon

5 Tuesday
Chinese New Year

6 Wednesday
Accession of Queen Elizabeth II

7 Thursday

8 Friday

REMINDERS

Saturday   9

Sunday   10

ORIENTAL PORK WITH EGG-FRIED RICE

Long grain rice 110g (4oz)
Sunflower oil 4 tsp
Boneless pork loin chop 225g (8oz), trimmed and thinly sliced
Carrots 2, peeled and thinly sliced
Green cabbage 110g (4oz), cored and finely shredded
Garlic 1 clove, peeled and crushed
Tomato ketchup 2 tbsp
Soy sauce 2 tbsp
Sherry or stock 2 tbsp
Ground ginger ¼ tsp
Spring onions 2, trimmed and thinly sliced
Egg 1 medium or large, beaten

1 Cook rice in a pan of boiling water for 10 minutes until just tender.
2 Meanwhile, heat 3 teaspoons of oil in a wok or non-stick frying pan. Add pork and carrots and stir-fry for 7 minutes. Add cabbage and garlic and stir-fry for a further 5 minutes.
3 Add ketchup, soy sauce, sherry or stock and ginger and stir together.
4 Drain rice, then rinse in hot water and drain again. Heat remaining teaspoon of oil in the pan, add onions and cook for 1 minute, then add rice and egg and cook, stirring, until egg scrambles. Spoon into warmed bowls with pork stir-fry and serve immediately.

Serves 2 • Time 20 mins
Calories 773 • Fibre 6.6g • Salt 2.6g • Sugar 2.5g
Fat 43.4g of which 10.2g is saturated

65

11 Monday

12 Tuesday
) First quarter

13 Wednesday

14 Thursday
St Valentine's Day

15 Friday

REMINDERS

Sunday 17
Septuagesima Sunday

CRANBERRY COCKTAIL

Ice cubes about 12
Good quality vodka 5-7 tbsp
Lime juice of ½
Sweetened cranberry juice
150ml (¼ pint)

1 Half fill a cocktail shaker with ice cubes.
2 Add vodka, lime juice and cranberry juice and shake well.
3 Strain into two chilled cocktail glasses and serve.

Cook's tips: Use orange-flavoured vodka with the cranberry juice; or replace cranberry with apple juice and add 2 teaspoons gingerbread syrup for a wintry drink (omit the lime).

Serves 2 • Time 5 mins
Calories 152 • Fibre 0g • Salt 0g • Sugar 8.9g
Fat 0g of which 0g is saturated

67

FEBRUARY

18 Monday

19 Tuesday
○ Full moon

20 Wednesday

21 Thursday

22 Friday

REMINDERS

Sunday 24

ROAST ORANGES & RHUBARB

Forced rhubarb 400g (14oz) cut into 4cm (1½in) chunks
Oranges 3, peeled and each sliced into 6 rounds, discard end slices
Caster or granulated sugar 6 tbsp
Thick plain yogurt or double cream to serve (optional)

1 Preheat oven to 220°C/200°fan/Gas 7. Line 2 large roasting tins with non-stick baking paper. Put rhubarb in one tray, orange slices in other tray, in single layers. Sprinkle 4 tablespoons sugar over rhubarb and 2 tablespoons over orange slices.
2 Roast fruit for 10 minutes. Check rhubarb; if not quite tender cook for another few minutes. Take rhubarb out of oven when just cooked. Leave oranges to cook for another 10 minutes, then turn off oven but leave in to crisp and colour.
3 Divide fruit between plates. Spoon over rhubarb juices and serve warm or cool with yogurt or cream.

Cook's tips: Use unwaxed oranges, washed and dried. This roasted fruit keeps well in the fridge for a week and is great to serve for breakfast with muesli or porridge.

Serves 6 • Time 30 mins
Calories 112 • Fibre 2.2g • Salt 0g • Sugar 21g
Fat 0.2g of which 0g is saturated

69

25 Monday

....

26 Tuesday
☾ Last quarter

....

27 Wednesday

....

28 Thursday

....

1 Friday MARCH
St David's Day

....

REMINDERS

Saturday 2

Sunday 3
Quinquagesima Sunday

GOAT'S CHEESE, HONEY & WALNUT TOASTIE

Sourdough bread 4 slices
Mild goat's cheese 110g (4oz), sliced
Walnuts 15-25g (½-1oz), chopped
Honey 2 tsp
Rocket leaves and pear slices to serve
(optional)

1 Preheat grill to medium.
2 Lightly toast bread on one side.
3 On toasted side of two slices of bread place cheese slices and walnuts and drizzle with honey. Place remaining bread on top, toasted side down.
4 Gently toast sandwiches under grill on both sides, until lightly toasted and cheese has softened. Serve with rocket and pear slices, if you like.

Serves 2 • Time 15 mins
Calories 428 • Fibre 4.3g • Salt 1.5g • Sugar 6.1g
Fat 24.8g of which 11.3g is saturated

71

4   Monday

5   Tuesday
Shrove Tuesday

6   Wednesday
● New moon
Ash Wednesday

7   Thursday

8   Friday

REMINDERS

Sunday 10
Quadragesima Sunday

CHICKEN & BROCCOLI PANCAKE BAKE

Plain flour 110g (4oz)
Eggs 3
Milk 425ml (15fl oz)
Vegetable oil for frying
Broccoli 150g (5oz), broken into florets
Soft cream cheese 110g (4oz)
Mature Cheddar 50g (2oz), grated
Cooked chicken 300g (11oz), cut into chunks

1 Sift flour into a bowl with a pinch of salt. Add 1 egg and gradually whisk in 300ml (½ pint) milk to form a smooth batter. Brush a frying pan with oil and make 8 pancakes with batter.
2 Preheat oven to 200°C/180°fan/Gas 6. Hard boil remaining eggs, then chop. Steam broccoli until just tender.
3 In a pan, warm soft cheese with remaining milk until just hot then stir in 25g (1oz) Cheddar. Mix half of this sauce with chicken, broccoli and hard-boiled eggs.
4 Divide chicken mixture down between pancakes and roll up. Place in a lasagne dish and pour over remaining sauce. Sprinkle with remaining Cheddar and bake for 25-35 minutes until hot all the way through.

Serves 4 • **Time 55 mins**
Calories 464 • Fibre 2.6g • Salt 0.8g • Sugar 0g
Fat 21.8g of which 10.2g is saturated

73

MARCH

11 Monday

12 Tuesday

13 Wednesday

14 Thursday
) First quarter

15 Friday

REMINDERS

Saturday 16

Sunday 17
St Patrick's Day

GUINNESS SODA BREAD

Butter for greasing
Wholemeal flour 450g (1lb), plus extra for dusting
Plain flour 150g (5oz)
Salt ½ tsp
Bicarbonate of soda 1½ tsp
Black treacle or brown sugar 1 rounded tbsp
Buttermilk 200ml (7fl oz)
Guinness or other stout 250ml (8fl oz)

1 Preheat oven to 220°C/200°fan/Gas 7 and butter a large baking sheet.
2 Mix dry ingredients in a large bowl. Add treacle or sugar, buttermilk and stout, mix with a knife, then use your hand to form a sticky dough.
3 Tip dough out and knead a little until smooth. Cut in half then form each piece into a round. Put on baking sheet, dust with a little wholemeal flour. Cut a cross in the tops and bake for 35-40 minutes until they sound hollow when tapped on the base.
4 Cool, then slice and serve with butter and honey or with smoked fish and a piquant salad, or with soup.

Cook's tips: Best eaten on day you bake it but fine toasted next day. Use honey instead of treacle or sugar for a sweeter tasting bread.

Makes 2 loaves • Time 50 mins
Calories 111 • Fibre 2.6g • Salt 0.2g • Sugar 0.8g
Fat 0.6?g of which 0.1g is saturated

75

18 Monday
Bank Holiday, Northern Ireland

19 Tuesday

20 Wednesday
Vernal equinox
Spring begins

21 Thursday
○ Full moon

22 Friday

REMINDERS

Saturday 23

Sunday 24

PORK & PRUNE PIE

Olive oil 2 tbsp
Pork shoulder steaks 4, trimmed of fat and cut into chunks
Plain flour 1 tbsp
Onion 1, peeled and chopped
Carrots 2 large, peeled and cut into chunks
Celery 1 stick, chopped
Bay leaf 1
Star anise 1
Pitted prunes in juice 290g can
Chicken or pork stock 450ml (¾ pint)
Shortcrust pastry sheet 320g pack
Egg 1 small or medium, beaten
Steamed green vegetables to serve (optional)

1 Heat oil in a large lidded non-stick pan.
Toss pork in flour, add to pan with onion and cook for about 5 minutes until pork is browned all over.
2 Add vegetables to pan with bay leaf, star anise, prunes (with juice) and stock. Bring to the boil, then reduce the heat, cover and simmer very gently for about 1½ hours until meat is tender.
3 Preheat oven to 200°C/180°fan/Gas 6. Remove star anise and bay leaf and, using a slotted spoon, spoon meat and vegetables into a 1.2 litre (2 pint) pie dish. Boil stock for 10 minutes to thicken, then pour over meat.
4 Cover with pastry sheet, trim to fit, crimp edges and decorate with trimmings, if wished. Brush with egg, make a hole in centre and bake for 25-30 minutes until pastry is cooked and golden. Serve with green vegetables, if wished.

Serves 4 • Time 2½ hrs
Calories 723 • Fibre 6.8g • Salt 1.4g • Sugar 4g
Fat 38.3g of which 12.7g is saturated

25 Monday

26 Tuesday

27 Wednesday

28 Thursday
(Last quarter

29 Friday

REMINDERS

Saturday 30

Don't forget to put your clocks forward 1 hour tonight

Sunday 31

British Summer Time begins
Mothering Sunday
Fourth Sunday in Lent

PEANUT BUTTER & POPCORN LAYER CAKE

Caster sugar 175g (6oz)
Butter 275g (10oz), softened
Treacle 40g (1½oz)
Eggs 3 medium
Self-raising flour 175g (6oz), sifted
Cocoa powder 5 tbsp, sifted
Milk 2-4 tbsp
Smooth peanut butter 110g (4oz)
Icing sugar 225g (8oz)
Sweet & salt popcorn 15g (½oz)
Toffee sauce for drizzling (optional)

1 Preheat oven to 180°C/160°fan/Gas 4. Grease and line three 18cm (7in) round sandwich tins.
2 Cream together caster sugar, 175g (6oz) butter and treacle until light and fluffy.
3 Beat in eggs, one at a time, each with 1 tablespoon flour.
4 Fold in remaining flour, cocoa and 2 tablespoons milk, then spoon into prepared tins.
5 Bake for about 20 minutes or until springy to touch. Cool on a wire rack.
6 Beat together peanut butter with icing sugar and remaining butter. Add 1-2 tablespoons milk, if necessary. Use to sandwich cakes together. Spread remainder on top, add popcorn and drizzle with toffee sauce, if using.

Serves 10 • Time 45 mins plus cooling mins
Calories 540 • Fibre 1.3g • Salt 0.9g • Sugar 43.7g
Fat 31.1g of which 16.6g is saturated

79

1 Monday

2 Tuesday

3 Wednesday

4 Thursday

5 Friday
● New moon

REMINDERS

Sunday 7

SARDINE SPAGHETTI WITH ROCKET

Spaghetti 250-300g (9-110oz)
Anchovy fillets in oil 50g can
Olive oil 1 tbsp
Garlic 1- 2 cloves, peeled and crushed
Dried chilli flakes a pinch
Fresh white breadcrumbs 6 tbsp (about 50g/2oz)
Sardines in olive oil 120g can
Lemon 1, finely grated zest
Rocket 4 good handfuls (75g-110g/3-4oz)

1 Add spaghetti to a large pan of fast-boiling water. Cook according to pack's instructions.
2 Meanwhile, tip anchovies with the oil into a large frying pan, then add olive oil, garlic and chilli flakes. Stir over gentle heat for 1-2 minutes until mushy. Turn up heat, add breadcrumbs and stir briskly until golden and crunchy. Tip onto kitchen paper.
3 Flake sardines with a fork straight into pan and add oil.
4 Drain pasta, reserving some cooking water. Tip it into frying pan, sprinkle in lemon zest, a little pasta water and half the rocket. Use tongs to toss together. Divide between four hot bowls and sprinkle each portion with more rocket and anchovy crumbs.

Cook's tip: Add some halved black olives and a squeeze of lemon juice, if you like.

Serves 4 • Time 20 mins
Calories 499 • Fibre 3.4g • Salt 1.5g • Sugar 0g
Fat 21.8g of which 3.0g is saturated

8   Monday

9   Tuesday

10 Wednesday

11 Thursday

12 Friday
) First quarter

REMINDERS

Saturday 13

Sunday 14
Palm Sunday

STEAK & CARAMELISED ONION CIABATTA

Butter 15g (½oz)
Olive oil 1-2 tbsp
Red onions 2, peeled and sliced
Balsamic vinegar 1 tsp
Rump steak 400g (14oz), trimmed and cut into fine strips
Steak seasoning 2 tsp (optional)
Ciabatta rolls 2, warmed according to packet's instructions
Rocket 15g (½oz)
Mayonnaise to serve (optional)

1 Heat butter and 1 tablespoon oil in a large frying pan over a medium-low heat and cook onions for 5-7 minutes until softened. Stir in vinegar and cook, stirring, until evenly glazed. Remove from pan and set aside.
2 Toss steak in seasoning, if using, then stir-fry in remaining oil over a medium-high heat until cooked to your liking.
3 Halve warmed rolls, spoon in onions, then top with rocket and steak. Serve with mayonnaise, if you like.

Serves 2 • Time 15 mins
Calories 393 • Fibre 6.2g • Salt 1.2g • Sugar 0g
Fat 25.4g of which 8.9g is saturated

83

15 Monday

16 Tuesday

17 Wednesday

18 Thursday

19 Friday
○ Full moon
Good Friday
Bank Holiday, UK

REMINDERS

Saturday 20

Sunday 21
Easter Day
Birthday of Queen Elizabeth II

MINI SIMNEL CAKES

Butter 175g (6oz), softened
Caster sugar 110g (4oz)
Eggs 2 medium
Self-raising flour 110g (4oz), sifted
Mixed spice ½ tsp
Dried luxury fruit 50g (2oz)
Marzipan 60g (2½oz)
Icing sugar 50g (2oz)
Ground almonds 50g (2oz)
Milk 1-2 tbsp
Sugar pearls to decorate

1 Preheat oven to 190°C/170°fan/Gas 5 and line a muffin tin with 9 paper cases.
2 Cream 110g (4oz) butter and caster sugar together until pale and fluffy. Beat in eggs, one at a time, each with 1 tablespoon flour.
3 Fold in remaining flour, spice and dried fruit and spoon into paper cases. Cut marzipan into 9 equal pieces and roll each one into a ball. Place in centre of each cake and push down slightly.
4 Bake for 18-20 minutes until risen and just firm to touch. Cool on a wire rack.
5 Cream together remaining butter, icing sugar, ground almonds and enough milk for a piping consistency. Use an icing bag to pipe onto each cake. Sprinkle 11 pearls on each.

Cook's tip: If you prefer, use a standard buttercream flavoured with ½ teaspoon almond essence instead of ground almonds.

Makes 9 • Time 45 mins
Calories 348 • Fibre 0.8g • Salt 0.5g • Sugar 25g
Fat 21.2g of which 10.8g is saturated

22 Monday
Easter Monday
Bank Holiday, England, Wales and Northern Ireland

23 Tuesday
St George's Day

24 Wednesday

25 Thursday

26 Friday
(Last quarter

REMINDERS

Saturday **27**

Sunday **28**
Low Sunday

TOAD-IN-THE-HOLE WITH SAGE & ONION

Vegetable oil 2 tbsp
Pork chipolatas 340g pack (12 sausages)
Plain flour 110g (4oz)
Eggs 2 medium
Semi-skimmed milk 300ml (½ pint)
Sage leaves 12
Onion 1, peeled and sliced into thin rings
Steamed broccoli and gravy to serve (optional)

1 Spoon 1 tablespoon oil into a small roasting tin. Put in oven while it heats up to 220°C/200°fan/Gas 7. When oil is hot add sausages, shake tin and cook for 15 minutes.
2 Meanwhile, put flour, eggs and half the milk in a large jug. Use an electric hand whisk to make a thick batter with lots of bubbles. Stir in remaining milk with plenty of salt and pepper.
3 Take roasting tin out, then quickly pour batter over sausages. Cook for 30-35 minutes until puffed up and crisp.
4 Meanwhile, heat 1 tablespoon oil in a frying pan, add sage leaves and fry for 30-45 seconds. Set aside. Add onion rings to pan, cover and cook over medium heat for 5 minutes, then uncover and cook until browned. Scatter onion and sage over Toad-in-the-Hole and serve immediately with broccoli and gravy, if you like.

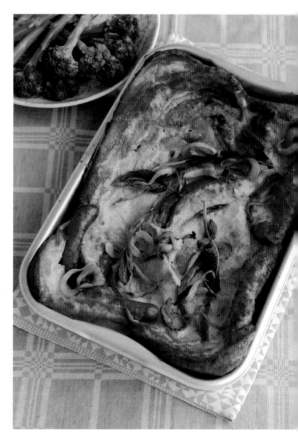

Serves 4 • **Time 60 mins**
Calories 494 • Fibre 4.3g • Salt 1.9g • Sugar 0g
Fat 30.9g of which 9.8g is saturated

87

29 Monday

30 Tuesday

1 Wednesday MAY

2 Thursday

3 Friday

REMINDERS

Saturday 4
● New moon

Sunday 5

ASPARAGUS MACARONI CHEESE WITH BACON

Streaky bacon 8 rashers
Fresh breadcrumbs 50g (2oz)
Cheddar cheese 150g (5oz)
Macaroni 300g (11oz)
British asparagus 2 bunches, trimmed and halved
Butter 40g (1½oz)
Plain flour 40g (1½oz)
Milk 400ml (14fl oz)
Dijon mustard 2 tsp

1 Preheat grill to high and cook bacon for 3-4 minutes on each side until very crisp. Chop and combine with breadcrumbs and a quarter of the cheese.
2 Meanwhile, cook macaroni in a pan of boiling water for 9 minutes then add asparagus and cook for a further 2 minutes.
3 Melt butter in a pan, add flour and cook for 1 minute, stirring continuously. Gradually whisk in milk to make a smooth sauce. Stir in mustard, some black pepper and remaining cheese.
4 Drain macaroni and asparagus and tip into an ovenproof dish. Stir in sauce and sprinkle with bacon mixture. Grill until top has melted and browned.

Serves 4-5 • Time 20 mins
Calories 595 • Fibre 4g • Salt 2.1g • Sugar 0g
Fat 28.1g of which 14.5g is saturated

6   Monday
Bank Holiday, UK

7   Tuesday

8   Wednesday

9   Thursday

10 Friday

REMINDERS

PINK GRAPEFRUIT SYLLABUB

Pink grapefruit 1 large, finely grated zest plus juice of half
Lemon juice 2 tbsp
Medium dry white wine 4 tbsp
Caster sugar 25g (1oz)
Double cream 300ml (½ pint)
Shortbread biscuit and grapefruit pieces to serve (optional)

1 Add grapefruit zest and juice, lemon juice and wine to a large bowl. Stir in sugar until dissolved. Cover and chill for 1-2 hours.
2 Pour cream onto juice mixture and whisk with a hand-held electric whisk until soft peaks form. Spoon into chilled glasses and serve topped with grapefruit pieces and with a biscuit, if you like.

Cook's tip: Substitute lemon for grapefruit to make a lemon syllabub.

Serves 4 • **Time 10 mins plus chilling**
Calories 429 • Fibre 1.3g • Salt 0g • Sugar 6.3g
Fat 40.4g of which 25g is saturated

91

13 Monday

14 Tuesday

15 Wednesday

16 Thursday

17 Friday

REMINDERS

Saturday **18**
○ Full moon

Sunday **19**

GNOCCHI WITH PEAS & MINT

Fresh gnocchi 500g (1lb 2oz)
Frozen petits pois 110g (4oz)
Courgette 1, trimmed and diced
Crème fraîche 150ml (5fl oz)
Dried chilli flakes ½ tsp (optional)
Chopped fresh mint 2-4 tbsp
Lemon 1, finely grated zest only
Parmesan or vegetarian alternative shavings to serve
Tomato salad to serve (optional)

1 Cook gnocchi with petits pois in a pan of boiling water for 3 minutes.
2 Drain and return to pan with courgette, crème fraîche, chilli flakes (if using), 2 tablespoons mint and lemon zest.
3 Over a low heat, stir everything together for 2-3 minutes.
4 Season to taste, scatter with Parmesan shavings and mint, and serve with a fresh tomato salad, if you like.

Serves 4 • Time 10 mins
Calories 351 • Fibre 4.1g • Salt 1.1g • Sugar 0g
Fat 16.8g of which 11.1g is saturated

93

20 Monday

21 Tuesday

22 Wednesday

23 Thursday

24 Friday

REMINDERS

Sunday 26
(Last quarter
Rogation Sunday

SMOKY CARROT SOUP WITH QUINOA & FETA

Vegetable oil 1 tbsp
Onion 1 small, peeled and chopped
Ground cumin 2 tsp
Sweet smoked paprika 3 good tsp
Carrots 500g (1lb 2oz), peeled
Vegetable Stockpot 1
Three colour quinoa 50g (2oz)
Feta cheese 110g (4oz)
Mint leaves a good handful
Balsamic vinegar for drizzling

1 Heat oil with onion and spices in a large pan. Cover and fry gently for 5 minutes while you coarsely grate carrots and add to pan. Cook, stirring occasionally, for a few minutes.
2 Add Stockpot and 1 litre (1¾ pints) boiling water. Simmer, half covered for 20 minutes.
3 Meanwhile, cook quinoa according to pack instructions, drain and set aside.
4 Whizz soup in pan using a hand-held stick blender and season to taste. It should be thickish but add boiling water to thin it down if you prefer.
5 Ladle soup into bowls, spoon a portion of quinoa in middle and crumble Feta on top. Tear mint leaves over, drizzle with vinegar and season with black pepper.

Cook's tip: For a spicier soup add a good pinch of chilli powder.

Serves 4 • Time 40 mins
Calories 185 • Fibre 6.8g • Salt 1.4g • Sugar 0g
Fat 10.2g of which 4.2g is saturated

27 Monday
Bank Holiday, UK

28 Tuesday

29 Wednesday

30 Thursday
Ascension Day
Holy Thursday

31 Friday

REMINDERS

Saturday 1

Sunday 2
Coronation Day

SPICY SWEET POTATO & PRAWN SALAD

Sweet potatoes 750g (1lb 10oz), peeled and diced
Extra virgin olive oil 3 tbsp
Rose harissa paste 3 tsp
Lemon 1, finely grated zest and juice
Raw peeled tiger prawns 250g (9oz), thawed if frozen
Pine nuts 75g (3oz), toasted
Baby leaf salad 1 bag (around 100g)

1 Preheat oven to 200°C/180°fan/Gas 6. Place potatoes on a baking tray and toss with 1 tablespoon oil and 2 teaspoons harissa. Roast for 15-20 minutes, until tender
2 Meanwhile, mix together remaining oil and harissa with lemon zest and juice.
3 Thread prawns onto skewers, brush with a little of the oil mixture and cook for 3-4 minutes each side on a hot barbecue or griddle pan.
4 Toss together potatoes, pine nuts, salad and dressing and top with prawn skewers.

Cook's tips: Use ordinary harissa if rose harissa paste is unavailable. To toast pine nuts: dry fry in a frying pan for a couple of minutes.

Serves 4 • **Time 20 mins**
Calories 411 • Fibre 6.5g • Salt 0.6g • Sugar 0g
Fat 22.2g of which 2.3g is saturated

97

3 Monday
● New moon

4 Tuesday

5 Wednesday

6 Thursday

7 Friday

REMINDERS

Saturday   8

Sunday   9
Whit Sunday
Pentecost

KIWI & LIME SORBET

Lime cordial 100ml (3½fl oz)
Caster sugar 75g (3oz)
Kiwi fruits 6, halved
Natural yogurt 150g (5oz)

1 In a small pan mix cordial with 200ml
(7fl oz) water and sugar. Bring to the boil
and simmer for 2 minutes until sugar has
dissolved. Bring back to the boil for 5
minutes more then leave to cool.
2 Scoop flesh from kiwi fruits into a food
processor, add yogurt and lime syrup and
blend until smooth.
3 Pour into a freezer-proof container and
freeze for 3 hours until slushy. Blend again in
the food processor and return to container.
Freeze for 3 hours or until ready to serve.

Serves 4 • Time 20 mins plus freezing
Calories 176 • Fibre 2.3g • Salt 0.1g • Sugar 23g
Fat 1.6g of which 0.7g is saturated

99

10 Monday

) First quarter
Birthday of Prince Philip, Duke of Edinburgh

11 Tuesday

12 Wednesday

13 Thursday

14 Friday

REMINDERS

Saturday 15

Sunday 16
Trinity Sunday
Father's Day

THAI RED CURRY CHICKEN BURGERS

Chicken thigh fillets 6 (about 615g/1lb 6oz)
Thai red curry paste 2-3 tbsp
Red onion 1 small, peeled and finely chopped
Coriander 1 pack (about 25g/1oz), stalks and leaves roughly chopped (reserve a few leaves to serve if you like)
Vegetable oil 2 tbsp
Dessert apples 2, quartered and cored
Lime 1, juice only
Fresh ginger 5cm (2in) piece, peeled and cut into very thin sticks
Mayonnaise 2 tbsp
Bread buns to serve

1 Use kitchen scissors to snip chicken into chunks straight into a food processor. Add curry paste, onion, most of the coriander and seasoning. Blitz until minced. Shape mixture into 6 or 7 large burgers.
2 Heat 1 tablespoon oil in a frying pan and when hot, fry burgers for 4-5 minutes each side until cooked through. Do this in 2 batches. Keep cooked burgers warm in the oven.
3 Cut apples into fine matchsticks and coat with lime juice. Add ginger and mayonnaise to make a slaw. Season well and add a few coriander leaves.
4 Serve each burger (with coriander leaves if you like) on a bun topped with apple slaw.

Serves 6-7 • Time 30 mins
Calories 386 • Fibre 2.6g • Salt 1.1g • Sugar 0g
Fat 17.3g of which 2g is saturated

17 Monday
○ Full moon

18 Tuesday

19 Wednesday

20 Thursday
Corpus Christi

21 Friday
Summer solstice
Summer begins

REMINDERS

Saturday 22

Sunday 23

FRAGRANT TEA-TIME TRAYBAKE

Green cardamom pods 10
Butter 175g (6oz), softened
Golden caster sugar 175g (6oz)
Eggs 3 medium
Self-raising flour 175g (6oz)
Icing sugar 110g (4oz), sifted
Rose water ½ tsp
Raspberries 150g (5oz)
Pistachio nut kernels 25g (1oz), chopped

1 Preheat oven to 180°C/160°fan/Gas 4 and line an 18 x 28cm (7 x 11in) traybake tin with baking paper.
2 Crush cardamoms with a pestle in a mortar, then pick out and discard husks. Grind seeds to ½ teaspoon of powder.
3 In a mixing bowl using a hand-held electric mixer cream butter, caster sugar and cardamom until light and fluffy. Beat in eggs one at time with a little flour. Mix in 2 tablespoons water with remaining flour.
4 Spoon mixture into tin and bake for 30-33 minutes until just firm to touch. Leave to cool in tin.
5 Mix icing sugar with rose water and 1 tablespoon water (or lemon juice for a sharper icing). Spread icing over cake then scatter over raspberries and pistachios.

Makes 18 squares • Time 50 mins plus cooling time
Calories 190 • Fibre 0.8g • Salt 0.3g • Sugar 15.8g
Fat 9.7g of which 5.4g is saturated

103

24 Monday

25 Tuesday
(Last quarter

26 Wednesday

27 Thursday

28 Friday

REMINDERS

Saturday 29

Sunday 30

WELSH LAMB WITH LEEKS & SAMPHIRE

Olive oil 1 tbsp
Welsh lamb leg steaks 4, at room temperature
Thyme sprigs 4
Butter 50g (2oz)
Leek 1 large (about 250g/9oz), trimmed and finely sliced
Spring cabbage or chard 150g (5oz), shredded
Samphire 110g (4oz)
Anchovy fillets 2, chopped
Capers 2 rounded tbsp, rinsed
Sherry 150ml (¼ pint)
New potatoes to serve (optional)

1 Heat oil in a large pan, season meat and add to pan with thyme. Brown steaks for 3 minutes on each side. Cover pan and cook for another 6-8 minutes until cooked to your liking. Remove with a slotted spoon and keep warm.
2 Meanwhile, melt half the butter in a large pan, add leek, cover and cook over low heat for 5 minutes. Add cabbage or chard, cook 4 minutes then add samphire; steam 2 minutes.
3 To make sauce, spoon off most of the fat from meat pan, add rest of butter along with anchovies and capers. Pour in sherry, then bring to the boil and reduce by half.
4 Spoon greens onto hot plates with steaks and spoon sauce over meat. Serve with new potatoes, if liked.

Serves 4 • **Time 30 mins**
Calories 444 • Fibre 4.4g • Salt 0.6g • Sugar 0g
Fat 32.1g of which 15.6g is saturated

105

JULY

1   Monday

2   Tuesday
● New moon

3   Wednesday

4   Thursday

5   Friday

REMINDERS

SYLLABUB TRIFLES

Rasberry jam 110g (4oz)
Trifle sponges 4, halved horizontally
Lemon 1, finely grated zest and juice
Caster sugar 50g (2oz)
Dry cider with elderflower 120ml (4fl oz)
Double cream 300ml carton
Mixed frozen fruits 200g (7oz), just defrosted

1 Spread jam over half the sponge slices and sandwich together with another slice. Place in 6 individual glasses, cutting to fit. Spread any remaining jam over the top.
2 Place most of the lemon zest, all of the juice and sugar in a bowl. Pour in cider and mix until sugar has dissolved. Drizzle a little over sponges until just moist.
3 Whip cream to soft peaks then gradually whisk in cider mixture.
4 Spoon fruit over sponges and top with flavoured cream. Sprinkle on a little lemon zest and then chill for 1-2 hours before serving.

Serves 6 • Time 20 mins plus chilling
Calories 450 • Fibre 0.7g • Salt 0.3g • Sugar 20.6g
Fat 30.9g of which 18.9g is saturated

JULY

8 Monday

9 Tuesday
) First quarter

10 Wednesday

11 Thursday

12 Friday
Bank Holiday, Northern Ireland

REMINDERS

ROAST PORK & HOISIN ROLLS

Boneless pork belly joint about 680g (1½lb), skin left on and scored
Olive oil 2 tbsp
Chinese five spice powder 1 tbsp
Burger buns or wraps
Hoisin sauce 2 tbsp
Spring onions 4, trimmed and finely sliced
Cucumber ½, cut into thin batons

1 Preheat oven to 230°C/210°fan/Gas 8. Check weight of pork and calculate cooking time: allow 45 minutes per 500g (1lb 2oz) plus 40 minutes.

2 Mix together oil and five spice and rub all over pork. Place in a roasting tin, skin side up. Roast for 10 minutes, then cover with foil and reduce oven temperature to 190°C/170°fan/Gas 5 and cook for remaining cooking time.

3 Remove from oven and leave to rest for 10 minutes. Remove any fat and thinly slice. Serve on burger buns or wraps, drizzled with hoisin sauce and topped with onions and cucumber.

Serves 6–8 • **Time 95 mins plus resting**
Calories 453 • Fibre 1.5g • Salt 0.7g • Sugar 2g
Fat 27.9g of which 9.1g is saturated

109

15 Monday

16 Tuesday
○ Full moon

17 Wednesday

18 Thursday

19 Friday

REMINDERS

Sunday 21

GOOSEBERRY & GINGER JAM

Fresh gooseberries 1kg (2lb 4oz) topped, tailed and washed
Fresh root ginger 50g (2oz), peeled and cut into 4 chunks
Lemon ½, juice only
Granulated sugar 1kg (2lb 4oz)
Butter 15g (½oz)

1 Put gooseberries, ginger, lemon juice and 150ml (¼ pint) water into a large, heavy-based pan. Bring to the boil, then simmer gently for 20 minutes, stirring occasionally, until softened to a pulp. Take off heat.
2 Stir in sugar until it dissolves. Add butter and bring to the boil. Bubble rapidly for 10 minutes then test for setting point by dropping a little jam onto a chilled plate. Push jam with your finger and if it wrinkles it's ready. If not, boil for a few more minutes and test again. Discard ginger.
3 Pour hot jam into warm, sterilised jam jars. Press a waxed disc on top, leave to cool then put on a cellophane disc and lid and label.

Cook's tips: Put a small plate in the freezer to chill before you start the jam. If using frozen fruit, add an extra 110g (4oz) fruit.

Makes 1.75kg (3¼lb)/4 jars • **Time 40 mins**
Calories 34 • Fibre 0.3g • Salt 0g • Sugar 8g
Fat 0.1g of which 0.1g is saturated

111

22 Monday

23 Tuesday

24 Wednesday

25 Thursday
☾ Last quarter

26 Friday

REMINDERS

Saturday 27

Sunday 28

JAPANESE CHICKEN & AVOCADO SALAD

Fresh ginger 1cm (¼in), finely grated
Miso paste 2 heaped tsp
Sherry vinegar 2 tsp
Rapeseed oil 2 tbsp
Cold roast chicken 250g (9oz), shredded
Pea shoots 4 handfuls (50g/2oz)
Avocado 1 large, peeled, halved and stoned
Lime 1, juice only
Pine nuts 2 tbsp, toasted
Thai red chillies 2, deseeded and finely sliced
Spring onions 2, trimmed and finely shredded

1 Whisk ginger, miso, vinegar, oil and 2 tbsp water in a mixing bowl. Add chicken and coat in dressing.
2 Scatter most of pea shoots over a platter or in a shallow dish. Spoon chicken and dressing over. Slice avocado, toss slices in lime juice then add to salad. Scatter with remaining pea shoots, pine nuts, chillies and spring onions.

Cook's tips: This makes a light salad. Serve with rice noodles to make it more substantial. Use watercress if pea shoots are unavailable.

Serves 4 • Time 15 mins
Calories 287 • Fibre 2.1g • Salt 0.1?g • Sugar 0g
Fat 20.8g of which 2.9g is saturated

JULY

29 Monday

30 Tuesday

31 Wednesday

1 Thursday AUGUST
● New moon

2 Friday

REMINDERS

Saturday 3

Sunday 4

BROCCOLI WITH FRESH TOMATO SAUCE

Olive oil 1 tbsp
Onion 1 large, peeled and chopped
Plain flour 1 tbsp
Vegetable stock cube 1, crumbled
Tomatoes 900g (2lb), skinned, deseeded and chopped
Broccoli 1kg (2lb 4oz), broken into florets
Fresh breadcrumbs 25g (1oz)
Cheddar cheese 25g (1oz)

1 Heat oil in a pan, add onion and cook gently for 7-8 minutes, until softened.
2 Stir in flour, stock cube and tomatoes. Bring to the boil then reduce the heat, cover and simmer for 30-40 minutes until thickened. Season to taste.
3 Meanwhile, preheat oven to 220°C/200°fan/Gas 7. Steam broccoli for 5-7 minutes until tender. Place in a small ovenproof dish.
4 Pour tomato sauce over broccoli and sprinkle with breadcrumbs and cheese. Bake for 25-30 minutes until browned and crisp. Serve as an accompaniment to meat or fish, or on its own with a crunchy salad.

Serves 4 • Time 1½ hrs
Calories 210 • Fibre 12.6g • Salt 1.6g • Sugar 0g
Fat 7.1g of which 2.2g is saturated

115

AUGUST

5 Monday
Bank Holiday, Scotland

6 Tuesday

7 Wednesday
) First quarter

8 Thursday

9 Friday

REMINDERS

116

Saturday 10

Sunday 11

PESTO TOPPED SALMON

Fresh white breadcrumbs 50g (2oz)
Grated Parmesan cheese 2 tbsp
Butter 25g (1oz), softened
Lemon 1, grated zest only
Pesto 2 tbsp
Salmon fillets 4, each about 150g (5oz)
Cooked new potatoes and peas to serve (optional)

1 Preheat oven to 200°C/180°fan/Gas 6. Mix together breadcrumbs, cheese, butter, lemon zest and pesto. Season to taste.
2 Place salmon fillets on a sheet of baking paper on a baking tray. Divide the topping between fillets. Bake in the centre of the oven for 12–15 minutes, until topping is a golden colour and salmon is just cooked.
3 Serve at once with new potatoes and peas, if liked.

Serves 4 • Time 25 mins
Calories 479 • Fibre 0.4g • Salt 0.7g • Sugar 0g
Fat 33.3g of which 9.3g is saturated

117

12 Monday

---

13 Tuesday

---

14 Wednesday

---

15 Thursday
○ Full moon

---

16 Friday

REMINDERS

Saturday 17

Sunday 18

CHERRY CHEESECAKE SQUARES

Digestive biscuits 8, crushed to a fine crumb
Butter 25g (1oz), melted
Soft cream cheese 280g tub
Natural yogurt 150g pot
Egg whites 2 medium
Caster sugar 3 tbsp
Plain flour 2 tbsp
Vanilla extract 1 tsp
Fresh cherries 150g (5oz), stoned and chopped

1 Preheat oven to 190°C/170°fan/Gas 5. Line a 20cm (8in) square tin with baking parchment. Mix biscuit crumbs with butter and press mixture into tin. Bake for 6 minutes. Leave to cool while you prepare filling and fruit.
2 Using an hand-held electric mixer, soften cream cheese in a bowl then add yogurt, egg whites, sugar, flour and vanilla. Whisk well.
3 Pour mixture into tin and place cherry pieces on top. Bake for 25 minutes. Leave to cool, then chill. Cut into 9 squares.

Cook's tips: Crush biscuits in a polybag with a rolling pin. Use blueberries, raspberries or apricots instead of cherries if you like.

Makes 9 squares • Time 45 mins plus chilling
Calories 219 • Fibre 0.8g • Salt 0.5g • Sugar 10.6g
Fat 12.9g of which 7.6g is saturated

19 Monday

20 Tuesday

21 Wednesday

22 Thursday

23 Friday
☾ Last quarter

REMINDERS

Saturday 24

Sunday 25

MOROCCAN LAMB KOFTAS WITH FRUITY SALAD

Lean minced lamb 500g pack
Red onion ½, peeled and finely chopped
Garlic 1 clove, crushed
Chopped fresh parsley 1 tbsp
Ras el hanout 1 tbsp
Cinnamon sticks 12 (optional)
Dried ready-to-eat apricots 50g (2oz), finely chopped
Pistachio nut kernels 25g (1oz), finely chopped
Red dessert apple 1, cored and finely chopped
Celery 2 sticks, finely chopped
0% fat natural yogurt 2 tbsp
Chopped fresh mint 1 tbsp
Warm pitta bread, little gem lettuce and pomegranate molasses to serve (optional)

1 Mix lamb together with onion, garlic, parsley and ras el hanout. Press mixture together around cinnamon sticks or onto skewers, if you prefer, then chill for 30 minutes or until ready to cook.
2 Cook under a pre-heated grill for 15 minutes, turning occasionally, or until cooked through.
3 Mix apricots, nuts, apple and celery with yogurt and mint and season to taste.
4 Serve koftas with fruity salad, pitta, lettuce leaves and pomegranate molasses, if you like.

Cook's tip: Ras el hanout is a spice blend, which can be found in most supermarkets.

Serves 4 • Time 25 mins plus chilling
Calories 333 • Fibre 2.6g • Salt 0.4g • Sugar 0g
Fat 20.6g of which 8.4g is saturated

121

26 Monday
Bank Holiday, England, Wales and Northern Ireland

27 Tuesday

28 Wednesday

29 Thursday

30 Friday
● New moon

REMINDERS

Saturday 31

SEPTEMBER Sunday 1

GADO GADO SALAD

Potatoes 450g (1lb), peeled and cut into chunks
Eggs 4 medium or large
Beansprouts 110g (4oz)
Fine green beans 110g (4oz)
Salted peanuts 50g (2oz)
Red chilli ½, halved and deseeded
Toasted sesame oil 1 tbsp
Onions 3, peeled and sliced
Garlic 1 clove, peeled
Soy sauce 1 tbsp
Lime 1, juice only
Sunflower oil 5 tbsp
Baby spinach 75g (3oz)
Cucumber 10cm (4in) piece, cut into batons

1 Cook potatoes in simmering water for 10-15 minutes then drain. Hard boil eggs, shell and quarter. Blanch beansprouts and green beans in hot water for 2 minutes then drain.
2 Meanwhile, make dressing; put nuts, chilli, sesame oil, 1 onion, garlic, soy sauce and lime juice into a blender with 5 tablespoons water and purée until smooth. Tip into a pan and bring to the boil. Cover and simmer very gently for 5 minutes. Gradually whisk in 3 tablespoons oil to make a thick dressing.
3 Heat remaining oil in a frying pan and cook onions for 10 minutes until crisp and golden.
4 Arrange all vegetables and eggs in four bowls and pour on dressing. Serve immediately.

Serves 4 • **Time 30 mins**
Calories 417 • Fibre 6.1g • Salt 1g • Sugar 0g
Fat 27.9g of which 4.5g is saturated

123

2 Monday

3 Tuesday

4 Wednesday

5 Thursday

6 Friday
〉 First quarter

REMINDERS

Saturday 7

Sunday 8

STEAK WITH TARRAGON BUTTER SAUCE

Vegetable oil 1 tbsp
Butter 75g (3oz)
Ribeye steaks 2 at room temperature, seasoned
White wine vinegar 2 tsp
Egg yolk 1 medium
Tarragon sprigs 4, leaves finely chopped
Chips and salad to serve (optional)

1 Heat a heavy frying pan on high until smoking. Add oil and 25g (1oz) butter. Fry steaks for 2 minutes on each side. Put on two warm plates, cover and set aside for 2 minutes.
2 Whisk vinegar, egg yolk and seasoning in a small bowl. Melt remaining butter in a microwave on high for 1 minute until bubbling. Quickly pour onto egg mixture whisking well until smooth. Put sauce back in microwave and cook for 10 seconds, whisk well, then cook for another 10 seconds for a thick sauce. Stir in tarragon.
3 Serve steak and sauce with chips and salad, if you like.

Cook's tip: Use rump or sirloin steaks if you prefer.

Serves 2 • Time 10 mins
Calories 530 • Fibre 0g • Salt 1.9g • Sugar 0g
Fat 44.8g of which 23.2g is saturated

125

SEPTEMBER

9 Monday

10 Tuesday

11 Wednesday

12 Thursday

13 Friday

REMINDERS

Saturday 14
○ Full moon

Sunday 15

CUMIN ROAST BEETROOT & SQUASH SALAD

Butternut squash 800g (1lb 12oz), peeled and cut into chunks
Raw beetroot 4, peeled and cut into chunks
Carrots 3, peeled and cut into chunks
Rapeseed or olive oil 3 tbsp
Cumin seeds 2 tsp
Dried chilli flakes ¼ tsp
Herb salad 1 bag
Hazelnuts 2 tbsp, chopped and toasted
Coconut or Greek natural yogurt 110g (4oz)
Lime 1, finely grated zest and juice
Toasted sourdough bread to serve (optional)

1 Preheat oven to 200°C/180°fan/Gas 6. Place vegetables in a single layer on a large baking tray and drizzle with half the oil. Sprinkle with cumin seeds and chilli flakes, season well then toss everything together. Roast for 30 minutes or until softened.
2 Divide salad leaves between four plates, spoon roast vegetables over the top and scatter with nuts.
3 Mix together yogurt and lime zest and spoon over vegetables. Drizzle with remaining oil, lime juice and season to taste. Serve with toasted sourdough, if you like.

Serves 4 • Time 40 mins
Calories 279 • Fibre 8.1g • Salt 0.9g • Sugar 0g
Fat 17.9g of which 2.9g is saturated

SEPTEMBER

16 Monday

17 Tuesday

18 Wednesday

19 Thursday

20 Friday

REMINDERS

Saturday 21

Sunday 22
☽ Last quarter

PORTUGUESE BAKED CUSTARDS

Grated orange zest 1 tsp
Caster sugar 1 tbsp
Egg 1 medium plus 1 egg yolk
Milk 200ml (7fl oz)
Ground cinnamon a pinch

1 Preheat oven to 180°C/160°fan/Gas 4. Put orange zest, sugar and egg plus egg yolk into a jug and whisk together.
2 Pour milk into a pan, bring it just to the boil and then gradually whisk it into egg mixture. Pour into two ramekin dishes and sprinkle with cinnamon.
3 Put dishes into a small roasting tin and pour enough boiling water into tin to come halfway up the sides of the dishes. Cook for 20–25 minutes or until custards are set. Leave to cool then chill before serving.

Cook's tip: For a variation, you could put a few raisins, blueberries or cooked fruits into the ramekins before pouring in the custard mixture.

Serves 2 • Time 35 mins plus chilling
Calories 149 • Fibre 0.8g • Salt 0.2g • Sugar 10g
Fat 6.8g of which 2.5g is saturated

129

23 Monday
Autumnal equinox
Autumn begins

24 Tuesday

25 Wednesday

26 Thursday

27 Friday

REMINDERS

Saturday **28**
● New moon

Sunday **29**

WIN A YEAR'S SUBSCRIPTION TO THE BOROUGHBOX DISCOVERY CLUB

The BoroughBox monthly Discovery Club is a curation of interesting and exceptional food and drink.

Each month the team of foodies choose their favourite items from the BoroughBox.com marketplace alongside secret and special items not widely available to buy. This little bit of foodie magic is delivered to your doorstep each month.

Enter now at **dairydiary.co.uk/win2019**
You can order your 2020 Dairy Diary via your milkman (see p170), or direct from the publisher at dairydiary.co.uk or by phoning 0845 0948 128 or 01425 463390.

30 Monday

Don't forget to order your **2020 Dairy Diary.** Use the order form on page 170 or order online.
If you don't have a milkman, call 0845 0948 128 or visit dairydiary.co.uk

1 Tuesday OCTOBER

2 Wednesday

3 Thursday

4 Friday

REMINDERS

Saturday 5
) First quarter

Sunday 6

CHICKEN WITH ROSEMARY & MUSTARD

Olive oil 2 tsp
Butter 15g (½oz)
Chicken legs 4, trimmed of excess fat and skin
Dry vermouth 150ml (¼ pint)
Hot chicken stock 300ml (½ pint)
Rosemary 3 sprigs
Double cream 6 tbsp
Dijon mustard 2 rounded tsp
New potatoes and fine green beans to serve (optional)

1 Heat oil and butter in a large shallow pan and brown chicken all over for about 5 minutes. Take chicken out and spoon off excess fat.
2 Heat pan juices, add vermouth and boil until reduced to 4 tablespoons. Pour in stock, add rosemary and chicken. Bring just to the boil, turn heat down, cover and simmer gently for 40 minutes.
3 Remove chicken and rosemary. Bring liquid back to the boil and reduce it by half, add 4 tablespoons cream, then reduce again until sauce just coats back of a spoon. Stir in seasoning, mustard and remaining cream. Put chicken back in to heat through, spooning sauce over. Serve with new potatoes and green beans, if you like.

Serves 4 • Time 1 hr
Calories 563 • Fibre 0.2g • Salt 1g • Sugar 0g
Fat 46.8g of which 22g is saturated

OCTOBER

7   Monday

8   Tuesday

9   Wednesday

10   Thursday

11   Friday

REMINDERS

Saturday 12

Sunday 13
○ Full moon

SPEEDY CHOCOLATE SPONGE PUDDINGS

Unsalted butter 150g (5oz), softened
Caster sugar 110g (4oz) plus 2 tsp
Self-raising flour 110g (4oz)
Baking powder ¼ tsp
Cocoa 2 tbsp
Egg 1 large
Vanilla extract 1 tsp
Dark chocolate 110g (4oz), broken into small pieces
Milk 3 tbsp
Vanilla ice cream to serve (optional)

1 Grease individual pudding basins or microwave-suitable teacups.
2 Place 110g (4oz) butter and 110g (4oz) caster sugar in a mixing bowl, sift in flour, baking powder and cocoa, then add egg, vanilla and 2 tablespoons water. With an electric hand-held mixer, mix ingredients together until smooth.
3 Divide mixture between pudding basins or cups, loosely cover with cling film and microwave on high for 4 - 5 minutes, until well risen and springy to touch.
4 To make the sauce: Put chocolate in a small bowl with the 2 teaspoons sugar, remaining butter and milk. Place over a saucepan of gently simmering water and stir until smooth.
5 Run a palette knife around each pudding then turn out onto individual plates and coat with sauce. Serve with ice cream, if you like.

Serves 4 • Time 20 mins
Calories 666 • Fibre 2.5g • Salt 0.4g • Sugar 46g
Fat 41.1g of which 25.1g is saturated

135

14 Monday

15 Tuesday

16 Wednesday

17 Thursday

18 Friday

REMINDERS

OCTOBER

Saturday 19

Sunday 20

CHEDDAR MUFFINS

Self-raising flour 300g (11oz)
Baking powder 1 tsp
Bicarbonate of soda ½ tsp
Caster sugar 25g (1oz)
Extra mature Cheddar cheese 150g (5oz), grated
Milk 300ml (½ pint)
Eggs 2 medium, beaten

1 Preheat oven to 200°C/180°fan/Gas 6 and line a 12-hole muffin tin with paper cases.
2 In a mixing bowl, sift together all dry ingredients, then add sugar and cheese and mix into flour.
3 Whisk together milk and eggs and gently fold into dry ingredients. Divide batter between muffin cases and bake for 18-20 minutes until well risen and golden. Serve warm or cold.

Makes 12 • Time 30 mins
Calories 170 • Fibre 1g • Salt 0.7g • Sugar 3g
Fat 5.9g of which 3.3g is saturated

137

21 Monday

(Last quarter

22 Tuesday

23 Wednesday

24 Thursday

25 Friday

REMINDERS

LOW & SLOW SHREDDED BEEF BRISKET

Lean brisket joint (unrolled) 900g (2lb)
Rapeseed or olive oil 2 tbsp
Chipotle paste 1 tbsp
Hot beef stock 200ml (7fl oz)
Chopped tomatoes with herbs 400g can
Runny honey 2 tbsp
Bourbon whiskey 3 tbsp (optional)
Red onions 2, peeled and sliced
Balsamic vinegar 2 tbsp
Caster sugar 1 tbsp
Bread rolls to serve

1 Preheat oven to 150°C/130°fan/Gas 2. Season beef all over. Heat half the oil in a large flameproof casserole and brown meat on all sides.
2 Add chipotle, stock, tomatoes, honey and whiskey, if using. Cover and cook in the oven for 3-3½ hours until beef is very tender.
3 Meanwhile, put onions in a small pan with the remaining oil and 2 tablespoons water, cover and sweat over a low heat for 10 minutes. Add vinegar and sugar and cook for a further 10-15 minutes until soft and syrupy.
4 Reserve any sauce and shred meat with two forks. Serve on rolls with sauce and caramelised onions.

Cook's tip: Add chopped carrots and red lentils to any leftover sauce. Simmer until tender and then purée into soup.

Serves 4 • Time 3½ hrs
Calories 424 • Fibre 0.9g • Salt 1g • Sugar 12g
Fat 19.4g of which 6.5g is saturated

28 Monday
● New moon

29 Tuesday

30 Wednesday

31 Thursday
Halloween

1 Friday NOVEMBER

REMINDERS

MONSTER MUMMIES CHOC CHIP SHORTBREAD

Butter 175g (6oz), softened
Caster sugar 75g (3oz)
Plain flour 175g (6oz)
Semolina 75g (3oz)
Green paste/gel food colouring
Milk or plain chocolate chips 50g (2oz)
White choco melts 160g pack
Candy eyes 20

1 Preheat oven to 200°C/180°fan/Gas 6 and line a baking tray with baking paper.
2 Cream butter and sugar together until light and fluffy. Fold in flour and semolina and enough food colouring to make a bright green. Stir in chocolate chips.
3 Tip out mixture onto a floured surface and shape into a log about 4-5cm (2in) diameter. Wrap in baking paper and freeze for 10 minutes to firm up.
4 Unwrap shortbread, slice into 10 and place on baking tray (they may crack a little but you can push them back together as you place them on the tray). Bake for 10-12 minutes until just firm then cool on a wire rack.
5 When cold, melt choco melts in a bowl over a pan of barely simmering water. Use to affix eyes, then drizzle over to create 'bandages'. Leave to set.

Makes 10 • Time 40 mins plus freezing and setting
Calories 324 • Fibre 1.1g • Salt 0.3g • Sugar 16g
Fat 18.9g of which 12g is saturated

4   Monday
❭ First quarter

5   Tuesday
Bonfire Night

6   Wednesday

7   Thursday

8   Friday

REMINDERS

Saturday 9

Sunday 10
Remembrance Sunday

CHICKEN & SWEETCORN SOUP

Butter 15g (½oz)
Spring onions 1 bunch, trimmed and sliced
Creamed sweetcorn 418g can
Frozen sweetcorn 110g (4oz)
Cooked chicken meat 175g (6oz), shredded
Chicken stock 750ml (1¼ pints)
Egg 1, beaten

1 Melt butter in a large saucepan.
2 Fry spring onions for 30 seconds.
3 Add creamed and frozen sweetcorn, chicken and stock.
4 Bring to the boil, cover and simmer for 5 minutes.
5 Bring almost to the boil, add beaten egg slowly, while gently stirring soup, to form egg threads. Cook until egg has set – do not boil. Season to taste and serve.

Serves 4 • Time 20 mins
Calories 163 • Fibre 3g • Salt 4.2g • Sugar 3g
Fat 6.6g of which 2.9g is saturated

143

11 Monday

. . . .

12 Tuesday
○ Full moon

. . . .

13 Wednesday

. . . .

14 Thursday
Birthday of the Prince of Wales

. . . .

15 Friday

. . . .

REMINDERS

CAFÉ NOISETTE

Coffee granules 3 tsp
Roasted chopped hazelnuts 2 tbsp
Granulated sugar 1 tbsp
Milk 300ml (½ pint)
Single cream 2 tbsp
Cocoa powder to serve (optional)

1 Dissolve coffee granules in 1 tablespoon boiling water. Pour into a blender.
2 Add hazelnuts and sugar and pour in milk and cream. Blend everything together.
3 Pour into a pan and heat gently until hot but not boiling.
4 Serve in mugs and sprinkled with a little cocoa powder, if you like.

Serves 2 • Time 5 mins
Calories 269 • Fibre 1.6g • Salt 0.2g • Sugar 7g
Fat 19.7g of which 4.5g is saturated

145

18 Monday

....

19 Tuesday
☾ Last quarter

....

20 Wednesday

....

21 Thursday

....

22 Friday

....

REMINDERS

Sunday 24

CHEESE & PECAN PALMIERS

Cheddar cheese 75g (3oz), grated
Pecan nuts 25g (1oz), finely chopped
Paprika ½ tsp
Cayenne pepper ½ tsp
Puff pastry sheet 320g pack
Egg 1 medium, beaten

1 Preheat oven to 200°C/180°fan/Gas 6. Grease a baking sheet.
2 Mix together cheese, nuts, paprika and cayenne pepper.
3 Brush pastry sheet with egg then sprinkle with cheese mixture. From long side roll one side in to centre. Repeat with other side until pastry rolls meet in middle. Cut across into 12 slices.
4 Place slices, cut side down, onto baking sheet. Bake for 15-18 minutes until crisp and golden. Cool on a wire rack.

Makes 12 • Time 30 mins
Calories 157 • Fibre 0.7g • Salt 0.5g • Sugar 0g
Fat 11.2g of which 48g is saturated

147

25 Monday

26 Tuesday
● New moon

27 Wednesday

28 Thursday

29 Friday

REMINDERS

Saturday 30
St Andrew's Day

DECEMBER Sunday 1
First Sunday in Advent

DUNDEE MARMALADE FLAPJACKS

Butter 175g (6oz)
Soft light brown sugar 75g (3oz)
Golden syrup 4 tbsp
Fine cut Dundee/Scottish orange marmalade 5 tbsp
Rolled oats 350g (12oz)

1 Preheat oven to 180°C/160°fan/Gas 4. Line an 18 x 28cm (7 x 11in) traybake tin with baking paper.
2 Cut butter into chunks straight into a pan, add sugar and syrup. Stir over a low heat and when melted remove from heat. Stir in 2 tablespoons marmalade, then oats.
3 Tip into tin, level out and press down well. Bake for 25 minutes until golden. Mark into squares, cutting almost all the way through. Spread remaining marmalade over as a glaze and leave in tin to cool.
4 Lift out of tin, then break up flapjacks along the lines.

Cook's tips: Pack cooled flapjacks in a freezer bag and freeze for up to a month. Marmalade with malt whisky can also be used. Add raisins or 1 teaspoon ground ginger if you like.

Makes 18 squares • Time 40 mins
Calories 196 • Fibre 1.6g • Salt 0.2g • Sugar 12.6g
Fat 9.6g of which 5.3g is saturated

149

2 Monday

3 Tuesday

4 Wednesday
⟩ First quarter

5 Thursday

6 Friday

REMINDERS

DECEMBER

Saturday 7

Sunday 8

SPANISH ROAST COD WITH CHORIZO & PERSIMON

Olive oil 2 tbsp
Chorizo sausage 75g (3oz), sliced
Garlic 1 clove, peeled and thinly sliced
Red onion 1, peeled and sliced
Spanish persimon 2, trimmed and sliced
Cod loin fillets 2 x 150g (5oz)
Smoked pimentón ¼ tsp
Fine green beans to serve (optional)
Parsley a few sprigs to garnish (optional)

1 Preheat oven to 190°C/170°fan/Gas 5.
2 Put 1 tablespoon oil into a roasting tin with chorizo, garlic, onion and persimon. Toss together then roast for 10 minutes.
3 Place cod fillets on top of chorizo mixture, drizzle with remaining oil and season with salt and pimentón. Roast for 10-12 minutes until fish is cooked through.
4 Serve with green beans and garnished with parsley, if liked.

Cook's tip: Smoked pimentón is a Spanish paprika found in the spice aisle. Use a sweet smoked paprika as an alternative.

Serves 2 • Time 30 mins
Calories 442 • Fibre 4.4g • Salt 2.3g • Sugar 6.6g
Fat 27g of which 6.9g is saturated

151

9 Monday

---

10 Tuesday

---

11 Wednesday

---

12 Thursday
○ Full moon

---

13 Friday

REMINDERS

GLUTEN-FREE MINCE PIES

Butter 110g (4oz)
Mixed dried fruit 110g (4oz)
Orange 1, finely grated zest and 4 tbsp juice
Cranberry or apple sauce 2 tbsp
Mixed spice 1 tsp
Gluten-free plain flour 175g (6oz)
Caster sugar 3 tsp plus extra for sprinkling

1 Melt 25g (1oz) butter in a large pan. Take off the heat, add fruit, orange zest and juice, sauce and spice. Use a stick blender to chop and mix ingredients together a little. Leave to stand for 30 minutes.
2 Rub remaining butter into flour and add sugar. Mix in 3-4 tablespoons cold water with a knife to make pastry. Knead lightly to a smooth cylinder.
3 Roll out pastry thinly in 2 batches between sheets of clingfilm. Cut out 12 x 6.5cm (2½in) rounds with a plain pastry cutter. Put them into 12 holes of a patty tin.
4 Fill each with 2 teaspoons fruit mix. Re-roll trimmings and cut out 12 x 5.5cm (2in) rounds or star shapes. Or rounds with star holes as per photograph. Press gently on top.
5 Chill pies while oven heats to 200°C/180°fan/Gas 6. Bake for 25 minutes. Sprinkle with caster sugar to serve.

Cook's tip: Use ordinary plain flour if you don't have a gluten intolerance.

Makes 12 • Time 40 mins plus standing
Calories 156 • Fibre 0.9g • Salt 0.2g • Sugar 3.2g
Fat 7.8g of which 4.8g is saturated

153

16 Monday

17 Tuesday

18 Wednesday

19 Thursday
☾ Last quarter

20 Friday

REMINDERS

Saturday 21

Sunday 22
Winter solstice
Winter begins

CHESTNUT, MUSHROOM & SHALLOT PIE

Butter 25g (1oz) plus 1 tbsp, softened
Shallots 12, peeled
Chestnut mushrooms 250 (9oz), quartered
Bay leaves 2
Rosemary 1 sprig
Cooked chestnuts 200g (7oz)
Red wine 200ml (7fl oz)
Vegetable stock 300ml (½ pint)
Plain flour 1 tbsp
Dijon mustard 2 tsp
Chopped flat leaf parsley 2 tbsp
Ready-rolled puff pastry 320g pack
Egg 1, beaten

1 Preheat oven to 200°C/180°fan/Gas 6. Melt 25g (1oz) butter in a frying pan and gently fry shallots for about 5 minutes until browned.
2 Add mushrooms, bay and rosemary; cook for 5 minutes. Then add chestnuts, wine and stock and bring to the boil. Simmer for 20-30 minutes until onions are soft. Remove bay and rosemary.
3 Mix remaining butter with flour and add to pan, stirring constantly until it dissolves, then cook for a further 5 minutes until sauce has thickened. Stir in mustard and parsley and season to taste. Spoon into a 1.2 litre (2 pint) pie dish.
4 Place pastry on top of filling, trimming to fit and crimping edges to seal. Cut a cross in centre, brush with egg and bake for about 20 minutes until golden. Serve immediately.

Serves 3-4 • Time 90 mins
Calories 629 • Fibre 8.3g • Salt 2.6g • Sugar 0g
Fat 31.4g of which 13.6g is saturated

155

DECEMBER

23 Monday

24 Tuesday

25 Wednesday
Christmas Day
Bank Holiday, UK

26 Thursday
● New moon
Boxing Day
Bank Holiday, UK

27 Friday

REMINDERS

Sunday 29

FESTIVE GLORIES

Double cream 150ml pot, softly whipped
Leftover Christmas pudding 200g (7oz), crumbled
Muscat or sweet sherry 8 tsp
Mandarins 4, peeled and divided into segments
Wild cranberry sauce 8 tsp
Stem ginger 2, cut into slivers
Pecan nuts 25g (1oz), chopped

1 With a hand-held electric whisk whip cream until softly whipped.
2 Divide half of pudding between 4 sundae glasses. Sprinkle 1 teaspoon wine in each glass. Top with half the mandarin segments, add 1 teaspoon cranberry sauce and a good dollop of cream. Repeat, then decorate with ginger and pecans.

Cook's tips: Use almonds or hazelnuts if you don't have pecans. Toast the nuts if you prefer. If you don't have much leftover Christmas pud, add some rich fruit cake or chocolate brownies.

Serves 4 • Time 15 mins
Calories 424 • Fibre 2.6g • Salt 0.2g • Sugar 30g
Fat 28g of which 14.7g is saturated

157

DECEMBER

30 Monday

31 Tuesday
New Year's Eve

1 Wednesday JANUARY
New Year's Day
Bank Holiday, UK

2 Thursday
Bank Holiday, Scotland

3 Friday

REMINDERS

Saturday 4

Sunday 5

CHESTNUT & PARSNIP DIP

Parsnips 300g (10oz), peeled and cut into small chunks
Olive oil 2 tbsp
Celeriac 300g (10oz), peeled and cut into small chunks
Cooked chestnuts 180g pack
Garlic 1 clove, peeled and crushed
Vegetable stock 200-250ml (7-9fl oz)
Bay leaves 2
Celery salt ½ tsp
Red chicory 4 heads, leaves separated
Smoked paprika (optional)

1 Add parsnips to oil in a large lidded pan. Fry over a medium heat for 3 minutes. Add celeriac, chestnuts and garlic and cook for 3 minutes, stirring occasionally.
2 Pour in just enough stock to cover vegetables and add bay leaves. Cover and cook on a low heat for about 25 minutes until all vegetables are tender.
3 Remove bay leaves and use a hand-held stick blender to purée. Season with celery salt and black pepper.
4 Arrange chicory leaves on a serving dish, spoon a teaspoon of dip onto each and dust with paprika, if you like.

Cook's tip: This purée is a great accompaniment to roast chicken, instead of potatoes. This quantity will serve 4.

Serves 8–10 • Time 40 mins
Calories 102 • Fibre 4.6g • Salt 0.3g • Sugar 0g
Fat 3.7g of which 0.6g is saturated

6   Monday
Epiphany

....

7   Tuesday

....

8   Wednesday

....

9   Thursday

....

10 Friday

....

REMINDERS

NOTES

NOTES

NOTES

NOTES

NOTES

NOTES

Three ways to order your Dairy Diary

FROM YOUR MILKMAN

Use the **order form overleaf**, or, if you usually order via your dairy's website, please order online.

TELEPHONE

If you do not have a milkman, call **0845 0948 128**, or **01425 463390**. Your diary will be posted to you.

ONLINE

Visit **dairydiary.co.uk**
See full details of the 2020 Dairy Diary and other great products.

DISCOVER MORE RECIPES & FABULOUS COMPETITIONS

Visit **dairydiary.co.uk**
Follow us on **Twitter** @thedairydiary
Follow us on **Facebook** dairydiary

Reserve your Dairy Diary 2020

To reserve your copy of the 2020 Dairy Diary, please fill in the form overleaf and leave it out with your empties from September onwards.

If you usually order via your dairy's website, please order online.

Order form overleaf...

Dairy Diary 2020

Order form

MILKMAN PLEASE LEAVE ME

☐ copies of the **Dairy Diary 2020**

☐ copies of the **Dairy Diary Set**

Name _____

Address _____

_____

_____

_____

Postcode _____

THANK YOU

Please leave out for your milkman from September 2019 onwards

MORE RECIPES AT DAIRYDIARY.CO.UK

RECIPE NOTES

- Nutritional information has been calculated by portion or item. Where there are portion variations, e.g. serves 6-8, the analysis given is based on the larger number.
- Spoon measures are level unless otherwise stated.
- Eggs are large unless otherwise stated.

V Suitable for vegetarians, provided a suitable cheese, yogurt or pesto etc. is used.

SAFETY NOTES

- Recipes using nuts or nut products are not suitable for young children or those with a nut allergy.
- Certain at-risk groups, such as pregnant women, babies and sick or elderly people should not eat raw or lightly cooked eggs.

F Suitable for freezing.

PLANNER 2020

JANUARY		FEBRUARY	MARCH	
1	Wed	BANK HOLIDAY	1	Sat	1	Sun
2	Thu	BANK HOLIDAY SCOTLAND	2	Sun	2	Mon
3	Fri		3	Mon	3	Tue
4	Sat		4	Tue	4	Wed
5	Sun		5	Wed	5	Thu
6	Mon		6	Thu	6	Fri
7	Tue		7	Fri	7	Sat
8	Wed		8	Sat	8	Sun
9	Thu		9	Sun	9	Mon
10	Fri		10	Mon	10	Tue
11	Sat		11	Tue	11	Wed
12	Sun		12	Wed	12	Thu
13	Mon		13	Thu	13	Fri
14	Tue		14	Fri	14	Sat
15	Wed		15	Sat	15	Sun
16	Thu		16	Sun	16	Mon
17	Fri		17	Mon	17	Tue	BANK HOLIDAY N. IRELAND
18	Sat		18	Tue	18	Wed
19	Sun		19	Wed	19	Thu
20	Mon		20	Thu	20	Fri
21	Tue		21	Fri	21	Sat
22	Wed		22	Sat	22	Sun
23	Thu		23	Sun	23	Mon
24	Fri		24	Mon	24	Tue
25	Sat		25	Tue	25	Wed
26	Sun		26	Wed	26	Thu
27	Mon		27	Thu	27	Fri
28	Tue		28	Fri	28	Sat
29	Wed		29	Sat	29	Sun
30	Thu				30	Mon
31	Fri				31	Tue

PLANNER 2020

APRIL		MAY		JUNE	
1	Wed	1	Fri	1	Mon
2	Thu	2	Sat	2	Tue
3	Fri	3	Sun	3	Wed
4	Sat	4	Mon BANK HOLIDAY	4	Thu
5	Sun	5	Tue	5	Fri
6	Mon	6	Wed	6	Sat
7	Tue	7	Thu	7	Sun
8	Wed	8	Fri	8	Mon
9	Thu	9	Sat	9	Tue
10	Fri BANK HOLIDAY	10	Sun	10	Wed
11	Sat	11	Mon	11	Thu
12	Sun	12	Tue	12	Fri
13	Mon BANK HOLIDAY	13	Wed	13	Sat
14	Tue	14	Thu	14	Sun
15	Wed	15	Fri	15	Mon
16	Thu	16	Sat	16	Tue
17	Fri	17	Sun	17	Wed
18	Sat	18	Mon	18	Thu
19	Sun	19	Tue	19	Fri
20	Mon	20	Wed	20	Sat
21	Tue	21	Thu	21	Sun
22	Wed	22	Fri	22	Mon
23	Thu	23	Sat	23	Tue
24	Fri	24	Sun	24	Wed
25	Sat	25	Mon BANK HOLIDAY	25	Thu
26	Sun	26	Tue	26	Fri
27	Mon	27	Wed	27	Sat
28	Tue	28	Thu	28	Sun
29	Wed	29	Fri	29	Mon
30	Thu	30	Sat	30	Tue
		31	Sun		

P.T.O. July–December 2020

PLANNER 2020

JULY	AUGUST	SEPTEMBER
1 Wed	1 Sat	1 Tue
2 Thu	2 Sun	2 Wed
3 Fri	3 Mon BANK HOLIDAY SCOTLAND	3 Thu
4 Sat	4 Tue	4 Fri
5 Sun	5 Wed	5 Sat
6 Mon	6 Thu	6 Sun
7 Tue	7 Fri	7 Mon
8 Wed	8 Sat	8 Tue
9 Thu	9 Sun	9 Wed
10 Fri	10 Mon	10 Thu
11 Sat	11 Tue	11 Fri
12 Sun	12 Wed	12 Sat
13 Mon BANK HOLIDAY N. IRELAND	13 Thu	13 Sun
14 Tue	14 Fri	14 Mon
15 Wed	15 Sat	15 Tue
16 Thu	16 Sun	16 Wed
17 Fri	17 Mon	17 Thu
18 Sat	18 Tue	18 Fri
19 Sun	19 Wed	19 Sat
20 Mon	20 Thu	20 Sun
21 Tue	21 Fri	21 Mon
22 Wed	22 Sat	22 Tue
23 Thu	23 Sun	23 Wed
24 Fri	24 Mon	24 Thu
25 Sat	25 Tue	25 Fri
26 Sun	26 Wed	26 Sat
27 Mon	27 Thu	27 Sun
28 Tue	28 Fri	28 Mon
29 Wed	29 Sat	29 Tue
30 Thu	30 Sun	30 Wed
31 Fri	31 Mon BANK HOLIDAY	

PLANNER 2020

OCTOBER	NOVEMBER	DECEMBER
1 Thu	1 Sun	1 Tue
2 Fri	2 Mon	2 Wed
3 Sat	3 Tue	3 Thu
4 Sun	4 Wed	4 Fri
5 Mon	5 Thu	5 Sat
6 Tue	6 Fri	6 Sun
7 Wed	7 Sat	7 Mon
8 Thu	8 Sun	8 Tue
9 Fri	9 Mon	9 Wed
10 Sat	10 Tue	10 Thu
11 Sun	11 Wed	11 Fri
12 Mon	12 Thu	12 Sat
13 Tue	13 Fri	13 Sun
14 Wed	14 Sat	14 Mon
15 Thu	15 Sun	15 Tue
16 Fri	16 Mon	16 Wed
17 Sat	17 Tue	17 Thu
18 Sun	18 Wed	18 Fri
19 Mon	19 Thu	19 Sat
20 Tue	20 Fri	20 Sun
21 Wed	21 Sat	21 Mon
22 Thu	22 Sun	22 Tue
23 Fri	23 Mon	23 Wed
24 Sat	24 Tue	24 Thu
25 Sun	25 Wed	25 Fri BANK HOLIDAY
26 Mon	26 Thu	26 Sat
27 Tue	27 Fri	27 Sun
28 Wed	28 Sat	28 Mon BANK HOLIDAY
29 Thu	29 Sun	29 Tue
30 Fri	30 Mon	30 Wed
31 Sat		31 Thu

ACKNOWLEDGEMENTS

Executive Editor
Nick Rowe

Managing Editor
Emily Davenport

Editor
Marion Paull

Art Editor
Graham Meigh

Front cover image
Kuttelvaserova Stuchelova

Production
Cath Linter

Recipes
Emily Davenport
Kate Moseley

Photographer
Steve Lee

Food Stylist
Sara Lewis

Props Stylist
Olivia Wardle

Recipe testing
Sharon Axson
Emily Bagshaw
Rachel Bark-Jones
Laura Pickering

Nutritional analysis
Paul McArdle

Special thanks
Aune Butt
Penny Meigh
Pippa Moore: *Spanish Persimon*,
Heather Munro: *British Asparagus*,
AHDB Beef and Lamb

Published by Eaglemoss Ltd

Electra House, Electra Way, Crewe Business Park, Crewe, Cheshire CW1 6GL

Dairy Diary orders telephone: 0845 0948 128 or 01425 463390

Queries telephone: 01270 270050

Website: dairydiary.co.uk

Email: enquiries@dairydiary.co.uk

ISBN 978-1-911388-13-5

PICTURE CREDITS

Front cover Shutterstock/Kuttelvaserova Stuchelova; 21 Depositphotos/GreenJo; 22 Shutterstock/sevenMaps7; 23 Depositphotos/victorburnside; 23 Depositphotos/nelsonart; 26 Shutterstock/Stefano Ember; 27 Shutterstock/Nicole S Glass; 28 Shutterstock/SpeedKingz; 32 Stock/SbytovaMN; 33 Shutterstock/AnikaNes; 33 Shutterstock/stockphoto mania; 34 iStock/RomoloTavani; 35 Alarmy/Dennis Frates; 36 Alarmy/Aga Baran; 37 GAPphotos/Clive Nichols; 38 Bokeh Photographic; 39 Shutterstock/GunnerL; 39 Shutterstock/Matej Kastelic; 39 Alarmy/MH Food; 40 Shutterstock/Y Photo Studio; 41 Paxton & Whitfield; 42 Shutterstock/udra11; 43 Paxton & Whitfield; 46 Shutterstock/HealthyLauraCom; 49 Shutterstock/Martin Novak; 53-179 Eaglemoss/Steve Lee except: 89 britishasparagus.com; 97, 127 makemoreofsalad.com; 139 image and recipe courtesy of AHDB from simplybeefandlamb.co.uk; 151 spanishpersimon.co.uk; 155 ukshallot.com